ice and fire

ice and fire

contrasts of Icelandic nature

text and pictures by
Hjálmar R. Bárðarson

PUBLISHED BY: HJÁLMAR R. BÁRÐARSON, REYKJAVÍK

FOURTH ENGLISH EDITION 1991,
ENLARGED AND BROUGHT UP TO DATE.

First English Edition 1971,
Second English Edition 1973,
Third English Edition 1980.

PUBLISHER: HJÁLMAR R. BÁRÐARSON.
P.O.BOX 998, 121 REYKJAVÍK, ICELAND.

PUBLISHED IN ICELAND AND COPYRIGHT © 1991,
BY HJÁLMAR R. BÁRÐARSON, P.O.BOX 998,
121 REYKJAVÍK.

ISBN - 9979 - 818 - 13 - 1

LAYOUT AND COMPUTER TYPESETTING:
HJÁLMAR R. BÁRÐARSON

COLOUR SEPARATION:
PRENTMYNDASTOFAN H.F., REYKJAVIK.

PRINTED IN ICELAND BY:
PRENTSMIÐJAN ODDI H.F., REYKJAVÍK.

SOME POINTS ON THE PRONUNCIATION OF ICELANDIC LETTERS

Most Icelandic place names and personal names in this book
appear in their Icelandic form. Of the Icelandic letters the
following might be mentioned:

Ð, ð is a voiced consonant pronounced like the **th** in English
weather.
Þ, þ is a voiceless consonant, pronounced like **th** in English
thin.
Æ, æ is a dipthong, pronounced like the **i** in English *like.*
Ö, ö has a sound that somewhat resembles the English vowel
sound in *bird.*
Á, á resembles the dipthong in English *house.*
Ó, ó somewhat resembles the dipthong in English *home.*
Ú, ú resembles the vowel sound in English *too.*
Í, í resembles the vowel sound in English *feel.*
É, é is pronounced like the English semi-vowel in *yes.*

It should be noted, however, that in some of these cases there
are only rough approximations.

ENGLISH TRANSLATION: SÖLVI EYSTEINSSON M.A.

Geysir in Haukadalur, (right) the best-known spouting hot
spring in Iceland, has given its name to other geysers all
over the world. In eruption it ejects a jet of boiling water and
steam 50 m up in the air, but now its eruptions occur only
very irregularly. Some Icelandic geysers, however, spout
quite regularly.

<<< THE FRONTISPIECE (p. 2) features a picture of
Hvannadalshnjúkur, the highest peak in Iceland, bathed in
the morning sun.

contents

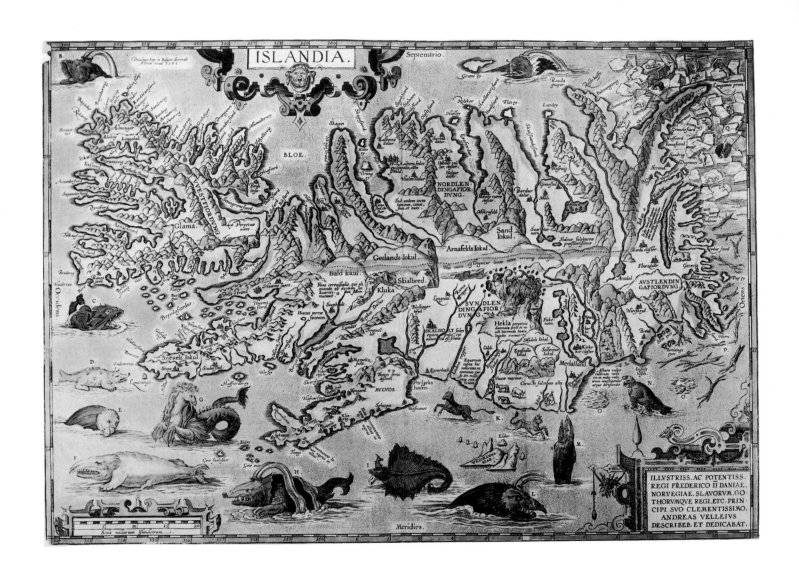

A map of Iceland, made by Bishop Guðbrandur Þorláksson of Hólar before 1585 A.D. The original drawing is lost. The illustration shown is reproduced from a printed version of 1590 which appeared in Additamentum IV, Theatri Orbis Terrarum by Ortelius. The sea ice northeast of Iceland is correctly located with reference to the ocean current boundaries. This is the first map that shows glaciers, and Mt. Hekla is shown to be erupting. The sea monsters, which are included for decorative purposes, were no doubt added by the editor. Bishop Guðbrandur, a pragmatic scholar as he was, is not likely to have appreciated this addition.

land of ice and fire

Iceland is often called a land of ice and fire. It was called Iceland because of the arctic drift ice which since the Norse settlement and down to recent years has occasionally more or less blocked the north-west, north and east coasts. The country could also be named after the glaciers, covering 11.5% of its area. But this northerly island, 103.000 km² (about 40.000 square miles) in area, just south of the Arctic Circle, has got fire below its surface, even underneath some of its glaciers. These remarkable contrasts of ice and fire are indicated on a map of Iceland, drawn by Bishop Guðbrandur Þorláksson before 1585. On this map the arctic drift ice is shown at Langanes, some glaciers are depicted on a map for the first time, and Mt. Hekla is shown to be erupting. In view of the small population of the country (250.000) and the immense areas covered by lava, volcanic ash, mountains and glaciers, the central highlands of Iceland are essentially virgin nature like an enormous national park. The glaciers and the visits of the arctic drift ice to the shores of Iceland make the name of the country fairly appropriate. At any rate, the Icelandic people appreciate its cold name although it is often emphasised that abroad the name gives a misleading impression of the climate, which is moderately temperate and considerably warmer than the position and the name of the country suggest because a branch of the Gulf Stream almost encircles it.

The settlement of Iceland is considered to have begun around 870 A.D. when the first Norwegian vikings sailed westward with their families and livestock. They found no inhabitants there, except a few Irish monks who had kept the old Greek name, Thule. The Norwegian settlers were accompanied by a number of Scots and Irish. The Icelandic nation, therefore, is basically of Scandinavian origin with an admixture of Celtic stock. In 930 A.D. the vikings established a legislative assembly, the Alþingi, at Þingvellir.

In 1262 Iceland acknowledged the sovereignty of the Norwegian Crown and together with Norway came under the Danish Crown in 1380. In 1918 Iceland became an independent sovereign state in personal union with Denmark through a common king, but has been an independent republic since 1944.

Ever since the settlement the history of the Icelandic people has been a record of a ceaseless struggle against the elements, severe weather, ice and fire. When drift ice closed the access to fishing and sea transport and spring came late, the cold weather caused great problems. On the other hand, there are 150 volcanoes in Iceland which have been active since the ice age, and about 30 of them have erupted since the settlement. During the last few centuries there have been volcanic eruptions in Iceland every fifth year on the average, and since about 1500 nearly one third of all lava flows on earth have been Icelandic.

The country is, therefore, one of the most active volcanic areas in the world, and in the past tephra falls and lava streams caused great damage, such as destruction of vegetation, followed by the death of livestock. When a volcanic eruption occurs under a glacier, the ice above the crater melts rapidly, resulting in floods, which sometimes lead to loss of life, although fatal casualties are less frequent than might be expected.

In the volcanic areas of Iceland there are 15 solfatara areas, and hot springs are found at about 700 places. The natural hot water is used for domestic heating on farms, in villages and towns, and for greenhouses.

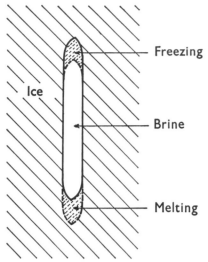

Brine cells can be spotted in ice floes. They are short vertical air-filled tubes in the ice, with both ends closed. They are formed when sea water is trapped in a number of small cavities when sea ice is formed. As more of the water freezes out of this brine, it becomes more and more concentrated and at the same time its specific gravity increases. Therefore, it moves downwards due to gravity and towards a higher temperature. Therefore, these cavities develop into short tubular channels in the ice because freezing occurs at the top of the cell while melting takes place at the bottom. This phenomenon is indicated on the sketch and shown below in the photograph of a stranded ice floe.

sea ice

Genuine sea ice is formed when the surface layer of the sea freezes. Most of the icebergs which sometimes drift towards Iceland with the sea ice come mainly from the Greenland glaciers. The icebergs, therefore, are developed on land by snow falling on the glacier year after year. This snow, in turn, is transformed into ice under the ever-increasing pressure from above. The valley-glaciers transport this ice into the ocean, and when the sea lifts the glacier snout, it breaks off and a new iceberg floats away.

Since 1950 it has been known that a third main type of ice exists in the seas, the so-called ice-islands. In the northern fjords of Greenland and off the north coast of Ellesmere Island thick floating ice sheets are attached to the coasts. These ice sheets are related to both sea ice and land ice. On the top of a sheet of sea ice which has not melted during the summer, snow accumulates year after year and then is gradually transformed into ice under pressure as on inland glaciers. These ice sheets, mainly consisting of fresh-water ice, can reach considerable thickness. When part of this ice sheet breaks off, an ice-island is born.

These ice-islands may often be 50 metres thick, 5 metres of which are above sea level. The biggest ice-island discovered so far is about 1000 km² in area. These ice-islands are often rather flat on top, but sometimes they have an undulating surface, reminiscent of landscape features. The name is therefore most appropriate, and at first these ice-islands were actually mistaken for real islands.

The ice formed at sea varies owing to different external factors, such as the salinity of the sea, the air temperature, wind and the speed of the formation of the ice. All sea ice consists of pure ice crystals, enclosing a large number of brine cells. If the ice is formed quickly, more brine will be enclosed in the ice. As more and more of the water in the brine cells freezes, the remaining brine will increase in concentration, resulting in increased specific gravity. The brine will, therefore, move downwards in the ice, both due to its weight and its attraction to higher temperatures. On close inspection these brine cells can be seen in the sea ice floes. The salinity in the upper part of sea ice is reduced more quickly at increased temperature, the reduction being very rapid when the temperature comes close to the melting point of the ice.

In hummocked ice on top of one-year-old sea ice the salinity is reduced to such an extent that this ice can be melted for drinking water.

This fact is of importance for expeditions in polar

regions, but experience taught the Eskimos this useful knowledge long ago. The mean salinity of the sea ice east of Greenland is considered to be about 50 ‰. It is obvious that the fundamental condition for the formation of sea ice is that the air temperature is lower than the freezing point of the sea, which has been reduced by the salinity of sea water. When the salinity is 35 ‰, the freezing point is about -1.9° C. Sea ice is formed much more quickly when the sea is stratified, so that on top of a layer with more salt content, which therefore is heavier, there is a less saline layer. If the difference in specific gravity is sufficient, only very limited mixing can take place between these layers even if the sea surface has cooled below its freezing point.

In this way ice can be formed on the sea although there is much warmer water a few metres below the surface. It is evident, therefore, that the different layers in the sea are at least as important for the formation of sea ice as low temperature.

In the North Polar regions the frost is severe, although not as intense as one might think. The frost very rarely exceeds - 47° C, but in the Antarctic - 75° C frost has been recorded. The North Polar region and the surrounding ocean is permanently covered by an almost unbroken sheet of sea ice, several years of age.

Following the life of a single ice floe, we find that it starts in the autumn when a thin layer of sea ice is formed on the surface. During the following winter the thickness increases until it has reached about 2 to 3 metres next spring. During the summer the brine will drain down through the ice floe, forming long vertical brine cells as explained above, and next autumn it has lost a considerable amount of its salt content. The sun melts the surface unevenly, forming water ponds. The sun warms the water in these ponds more than the dry ice hummocks and therefore more melting takes place around the ponds. Part of the melt-water is discharged into the sea. The following winter additional layers will freeze at the bottom of the ice floe. If the floe survives through the summer, additional layers will freeze to its lower surface the following winter, and so on in a continuous cycle: During the summer ice melts on top of the floe, whereas the following winter will lead to fresh ice formation at the bottom.

After a period of a few years an equilibrium is reached, and while it lasts the thickness of the ice floe will remain 3-4 metres.

An ice cube in the floe will thus be moving, from the time it is formed at the bottom, up to the top, where it will finally melt and the resulting water flow back into the sea. Although the mean thickness of arctic ice is about 3.5 metres, it can reach a thickness of more than 5 metres.

Scattered ice floes drifting off Straumnes near Aðalvík on the north-west coast of Iceland on March 24, 1968.

drift ice

A look at a terrestrial globe makes it obvious that there is a great difference between the North and South Polar regions. The South Pole is on a vast continent, mostly covered with ice and snow, about 4800 km wide, surrounded by the Atlantic, Pacific and Indian Oceans. The North Pole on the other hand, is situated in a large ocean area, about 3200 km wide, but it has connections with both the Atlantic and the Pacific Oceans. The North Pole itself is near the middle of this Arctic Ocean, where the depth of the water is about 4000 meters. It was mentioned above (page 9) that much lower temperature is found in the South Polar region than at the North Pole. The reason is the geographical difference as extreme cold is found above high continents, not above the oceans.

In the northern hemisphere the coldest place in winter is not at the North Pole, but in Northern Siberia. The 65°parallel runs through the middle of Iceland, the Norwegian sea, the middle of Norway, through Russia, North Siberia, the Bering Sea, Alaska, Canada, Baffin Bay, Southern part of Greenland and the Greenland Sea.

Along this parallel the climate varies enormously. Here we do not only have differences in climate between land and sea areas. The climatic conditions of the sea areas themselves differ substantially. The difference is particularly marked between the eastern and western parts of the Atlantic Ocean. This is clearly indicated on the ocean current map right (on page 11).

The cold Labrador Current is dominant off the east coast of Canada, whereas the warm Gulf Stream with its extension, the North Atlantic Current and its branches, carries warm water up to the coasts of Iceland and Norway and further on to Spitsbergen and the Barent Sea, keeping the ocean free from ice far to the north. It is mainly due to these warm sea currents that the coasts of Iceland are usually completely ice-free most winters and that the climate there is a cold-temperate oceanic climate in spite of the fact that the country is situated just south of the Arctic Circle.

But from the North Polar sea comes the very cold East-Greenland Current through the channel between North-Greenland and Spitsbergen, which is the main connection between the North Polar region and the North Atlantic Ocean. This current brings large amounts of sea ice, which is sometimes carried up to the Icelandic coasts. Therefore, oceanographically Iceland is also a country of contrasts.

Off its coasts the cold and warm sea currents meet, the cold Polar Current from the north, and the warm Atlantic Current from the south. Opposite natural forces, air and sea currents, continuously influence the weather with varying effects, resulting in the capricious climate Iceland is known for.

Although an ice cover persists in the Arctic all the year round, it is always on the move and is, therefore, called drift ice. In August the amount of ice is usually at a minimum, but even then it covers an area that is about four times as large as Greenland.

The Arctic is essentially an enclosed sea area, about 3200 km wide, with straits or channels leading to the Atlantic and Pacific Oceans. The map shows the ice border during those months of an average year when the ice has reached its maximum and minimum extent respectively.

By March the drift ice has filled the space up to the coastal ice around the North Polar region. Then the sea ice covers an area that is twice as large as the ice cover in August.

This drift ice is far from being a flat, continuous ice sheet. Due to the action of wind and sea currents the ice is broken up into big or small floes. Since the currents are irregular and the floes vary greatly in size, they move neither at the same speed nor in the same direction. Therefore, open sea is very common between the floes and sometimes there are long narrow leads. In summer fairly large ice-free areas in the drift ice where submarines can get to the surface are quite common, but with the advent of winter the floes very soon freeze together. This ice, however, is soon broken into floes again due to the movement of the sea. When no open sea area is left and the drift ice is on the move, the floes either slide over each other or are raised on edge under heavy pressure. Camping on a floe in fast-moving drift ice is, therefore, not without danger. The sea currents are the main moving force, although the wind also plays a part.

Research on the movement of the sea ice in this region started about 85 years ago, first on board ships drifting with the ice, but later by means of floating research stations on ice floes.

The first successful expedition by a ship drifting in the ice was the FRAM expedition of 1893-6, headed by Fridtjof Nansen. The ship started from the mouth of the river Lena, and for three years it drifted without any damage, locked in the ice, until it got free of the ice near Spitsbergen. FRAM, therefore, drifted over the entire North Polar sea on the Siberian side of the North Pole. In the years 1937-40 the Russian ice-breaker SEDOV drifted along a similar route as the FRAM had done before, and several other ships have drifted shorter distances, the purpose being to study the movement of the ice.

The development of aviation opened up a completely new possibility for this research. The first landing and take-off on an ice floe took place in 1927, but today such landings no longer make headlines as aircraft have brought supplies to several research stations on ice floes or ice-islands, manned by American or Russian scientists for 12 to 18 months at a time.

During these periods weather and exact movements of the ice have been registered. Finally, by means of nuclear submarines it is now possible to navigate under the ice across the North Polar region for a closer study of the ocean and of the sea ice from below.

Sea ice is a surprisingly plastic material. If the upper surface of an ice floe is covered with ridges and the bottom surface is smooth, then after some time corresponding ridges will develop on the bottom to the extent that every hummock on the top will be lowered until a complete equilibrium is reached when the relief at the bottom is 8 to 9 times as large as the corresponding one on the top.

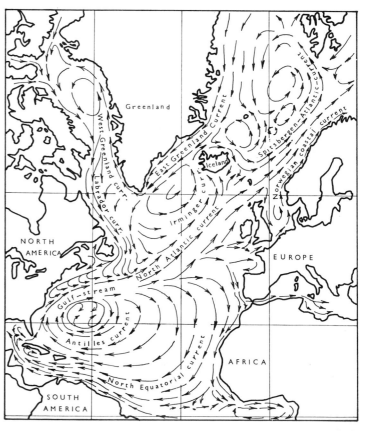

A map of the currents of the North-Atlantic shows how the warm Gulf Stream sends the North-Atlantic Current and its branches up to the coasts of Iceland and Norway, thereby maintaining ice-free areas far to the north. The East-Greenland Current, on the other hand, brings with it large quantities of sea ice which sometimes drifts up to the coast of Iceland.

the sea ice and Iceland

Sinee the settlement of Iceland the sea ice has been an integral part of its history. An account of the settlement of Nordic vikings in Iceland is given in the unique Book of Settlements (*Landnámabók*). The beginning of the Landnámabók has the following passage: 'In the book of history by the Venerable Bede there is a reference to an island called Thile (Thule), and it is reported in books to be a six days' voyage to the north of Britain; he says there are no days there in winter and no nights in summer when the day is longest.Wise men believe that Thile is Iceland, as in many places in the country the sun shines during the night when the day is longest, and in some places the sun cannot be seen when the nights are the longest.'... In the Landnámabók we are also told that before Iceland was settled from Norway there were people in the country, whom the Norwegians called Papar. They were Christians and are believed to have been Irish hermits. It is also said that when Iceland´ was settled from Norway, Adrianus was Pope in Rome. Adrianus II was Pope in 867- 72.

The first Nordic men to come to Iceland were the vikings Naddoddur and Garðar Svavarsson. Naddoddur was sailing from Norway to the Faroes when he and his men drifted westward and found a big land. They climbed a mountain on the east coast to look if they could see any smoke or other signs of human habitation, but they found none. When they left the country some snow fell on the mountains, and therefore they called the country *Snæland* (Snowland).

Garðar Svavarsson was of Swedish origin. He went to the Hebrides to fetch his wife´s paternal inheritance. When sailing through the Pentland Fjord, wind and sea carried his ship westwards. He came to Iceland, sailed around it and thus found it was an island. During the winter he stayed at a place he called Húsavík (House-wick). Garðar Svavarsson sailed eastward to Norway. He praised the country and called it *Garðarshólmi*.

A viking called Flóki Vilgerðarson sailed from Ryvarden in Norway to search for Garðarshólmi. First he sailed to the Shetland Islands and then to the Faroes. From there he sailed to Iceland, passed Snæfellsnes, then crossed Breiðafjörður and landed at Vatnsfjörður on Barðaströnd. On his Iceland voyage we have the following passage in the Landnámabók (Manuscript: Sturlubók, AM 107 fol.): 'Then fish was abundant in the fjord, and they were so busy catching it that they forgot to make hay during the summer and therefore all their livestock died the following winter.

The spring was rather cold. Then Flóki Vilgerðarson climbed a high mountain, and from there he could see a fjord filled with drift ice, and therefore they called the country Iceland, which has been its name ever since.

Close to a river in Vatnsfjörður there still remain foundations of old walls believed to be from the buildings erected by Flóki Vilgerðarson when he spent a winter there about the year 856 A.D. Usually there is not much snow in this area, Barðaströnd, and drift ice is very seldom found there. Flóki Vilgerðarson could have seen drift ice from the mountains near Vatnsfjörður and also in Patreksfjörður or Arnarfjörður (see picture on p. 90). It is, however, more likely that he explored the land further and saw drift ice on Steingrímsfjörður or Húnaflói. It would have been only natural to call the country Iceland after seeing a fjord like Steingrímsfjörður filled with drift ice (see picture on page 15).

The following winter Flóki Vilgerðarson stayed in Borgarfjörður and then returned to Norway. He spoke ill of the country, but his men reported both its good and bad features.

The first settlers in Iceland must have got acquainted with the drift ice right from the very beginning, and Icelandic poets have called it 'Iceland´s age-old foe.' Most likely the first settlers soon discovered that the name of the country discouraged immigration, and therefore they named the next country they discovered Greenland when they later, about 985-86, continued further westwards because they believed more people would like to leave Iceland for the new land if it had an attractive name.

Landnámabók ('Book of Settlements') has been preserved in 5 versions, three of which are old, while two are 17th century copies. A vellum manuscript of Sturlubók, written in the 13th century by Sturla Þórðarson, was destroyed by fire in Copenhagen in 1728, but before the original was sent abroad it was copied by the Rev. Jón Erlendsson of Villingaholt. The illustration (right) is of the page in his copy (AM 107 fol.) which describes the voyage of Flóki Vilgerðarson and his stay in Iceland when he gave it the name which it has borne ever since.

at þeir sa Snæfells nes þa rædde þeir vm. þetta
mun vera mikit land er var haufum fundit. her eru
vatnfaull stor. siþ er þat kalladur faxa os. þeir
Floki siglðu vestur yfer Breidafiord. ok toku þar
land sem heiter vaz fiordur vid Barda strond. þa
var fiordurin fullur af veidiskap. Ok gaðu er eigi fyr'
veidum at þa heyiaða ok do allt kuikfe þeira vm vetrin
vor var helldur kallt. þa gekk Floki vppa fiall eitt hatt
ok sa norður yfir fiollin fiord fullan af hafisum. þi kaull
uðu þeir landit Island sem þat hefer siþ heitit.
þeir Floki ætluðu brutt vm sumarit. ok vrðu bunir litlu
þ vetur. þeim beit ei fyrir Reykianes ok sleit þa þeim
batin ok þar an Heriolf. hn tok þar sem nu heiter Heriolfs
haufn. Floki var vm veturin j Borgarfirdi. ok
fundu þeir Heriolf. þeir siglðu vm sumarit eft 't Nor
egs. Ok er m spurðu af landinu þa let Floki illa yfer
en Heriolfur sagde kost ok laust af landinu. En þor
olfur buið driupa smior af hveriu strae a landinu
þvi er þeir haufðu fundit. þvi var hn kalladur þor
olfur smior.

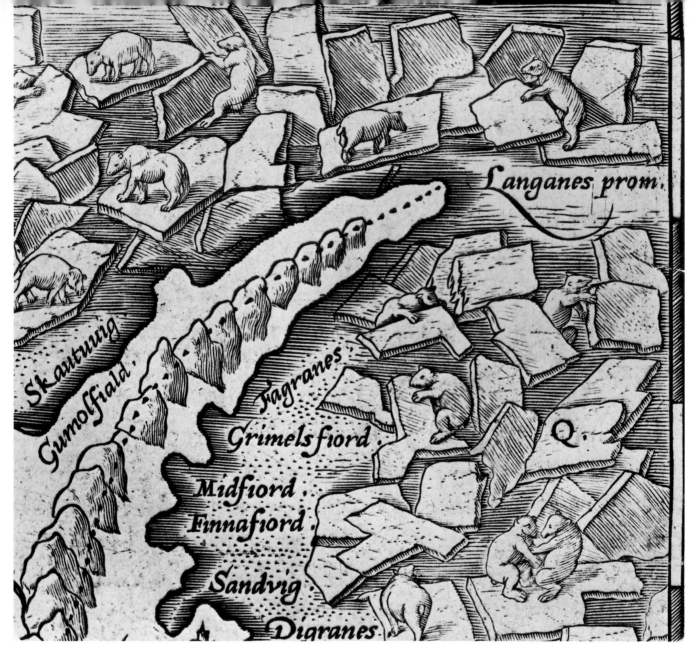

Part of a map of Iceland, drawn by Bishop Guðbrandur Þorláksson before 1585. It shows sea ice and polar bears off Langanes. In explanations under Q on the back of the map it is stated that great quantities of sea ice are carried by currents from the ice-covered ocean to the coasts of Iceland. It is also said that the movement of the ice floes makes a lot of noise and that some of the floes are packed with polar bears at play. The entire map is featured on page 2. The place names are easily recognizable, although the lithographer seems to have corrupted the original manuscript in respect of some.

Landnámabók (Book of Settlements) states that Flóki Vilgerðarson gave Iceland its name after climbing a high mountain from which he saw across the mountains in the north a fjord full of ice. It is only natural that he should give the country such a name if he saw a fjord like Steingrímsfjörður as it appears in this picture (right), taken on May 8, 1969.

It is believed that the sea ice did not do much harm during the first few centuries after the settlement, which started about 870. News was brought to Norway about the good land in the west. It was said that Iceland was covered with woods from the mountains to the sea. Fish was plentiful in the fjords and salmon and trout abounded in rivers and lakes. There was also an abundance of birds and eggs and drift-wood all over the shores.

It It is usually said that the settlement period was over by the time the Alþingi, the legislative asssembly, was established at Þingvellir about 930 A.D. In the year 1000 Christianity was adopted by law at the Alþingi, and when the collection of tithes was begun by the church in 1096, the total population of the country is estimated to have been 70-80 thousand. When the Icelanders accepted allegiance to the King of Norway in 1262, the old Icelandic commonwealth and the so-called golden age of Iceland´s history came to an end. It is generally assumed that during this period the country enjoyed considerable prosperity. Besides, this was the time that generated the highly acclaimed Icelandic family sagas.

It was followed by times of great adversity and hardship. Volcanic eruptions caused a loss of life and property and the sea ice made more frequent visits.

Old annals make frequent references to these tribu-lations. People who rely for their living to a considerable extent on livestock are generally very dependent on the weather and other environmental factors. In 1380 Iceland, together with Norway, came under the Danish Crown. All foreign and domestic trade was monopolized by the Danes between 1602 and 1787. Therefore, external circumstances and weather conditions combined to make very hard times for the Icelandic nation. But the 19th and 20th centuries brought great improvements with increased self-government and eventual independence together with more diversified industries and progressively improved technical skills as well as a milder climate. It is important to bear these historical facts in mind when we look to the past in an attempt to study the visits of the drift ice to the coasts of Iceland. It is evident that from the very beginning the Icelanders became familiar with much of the nature of the drift ice north of Iceland and on the seafarers' routes from Iceland to the new settlements on the west coast of Greenland. In the

Sea ice is also endowed with certain beauty, both in form and colours (left), although the cold it brings usually comes first to one´s mind.

book *Konungsskuggsjá* ('The King's Mirror'), dating from about 1260, there is a very interesting passage on the drift ice off Iceland: '...when going far enough out into the high sea, we come upon such large amounts of ice in the sea that I do not know any other similar place in the whole world. Parts of this ice are so flat that they must have frozen on the sea itself, eight to ten feet thick, and they extend so far from the coast that a journey on foot from land to the edge of the ice would take four days or more... This ice is of a peculiar character. Sometimes it does not move at all, the floes being separated by open sea or fjords, but sometimes their speed is so high that they move no slower than a ship sailing before a good wind. And when they move, they sail just as often against the wind as before it.

Some of the ice in the ocean is of a different shape. The Greenlanders call it 'tumbling glaciers'. Their form is like that of big mountains, rising up above the sea level, but they keep company with any other ice although sometimes they travel by themselves'. This description of the ice floes and icebergs is in many ways correct. Then, as now, the drift ice followed the east coast of Greenland, and the movement of the ice was a riddle that long beggared solution.

Historical information on the sea ice off Iceland varies a good deal. Sources from written stories about persons and places are naturally of limited value as they only describe climate and drift ice in relation to certain happenings. Although such information may certainly be very interesting as evidence of the movement of the sea ice up to the Icelandic coast, its value is not extensive in view of the amount of sea ice approaching the coast from year to year. The annals, therefore, are in this respect better sources, and not many other places in the world are likely to have more reliable information on sea ice over such a long period of time.

Of course, the interest of the different annalists in the climate and in sea ice varies substantially at different times and places. Therefore, a great deal of work is required to evaluate the sources in such a way that the most correct general view is obtained. The annals use language sparingly, but they contain concentrated information. *Lögmannsannal* can be quoted as an example: Year 1371 : Rather serious famine and a hard winter. Year 1374: Winter and spring so hard that no one could remember anything like it in Northern Iceland. No growth of grass, sea ice at the coast until Bartholomew Mass on August 24. Year 1375: Winter so good that no one could remember another like it. There is a marked gap in the information on the drift ice off Iceland during the 15th century and the beginning of the 16th. One of the best extant general accounts of sea ice, however, is to be found in the description of Iceland by Oddur Einarsson,

	JAN	FEB	MAR	APR	MAY	JUNE		JULY	AUG	SEPT	OCT	NOV	DEC

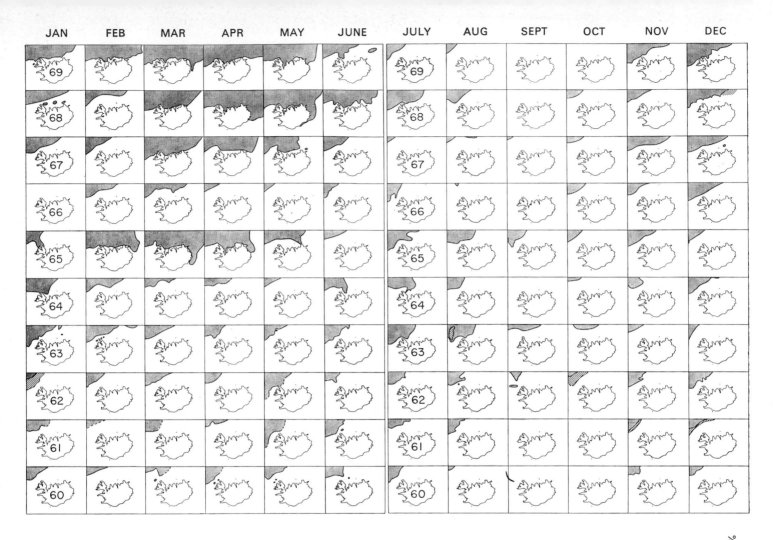

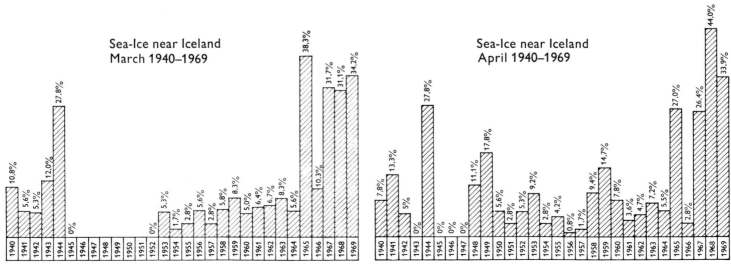

Sea-Ice near Iceland
March 1940–1969

Sea-Ice near Iceland
April 1940–1969

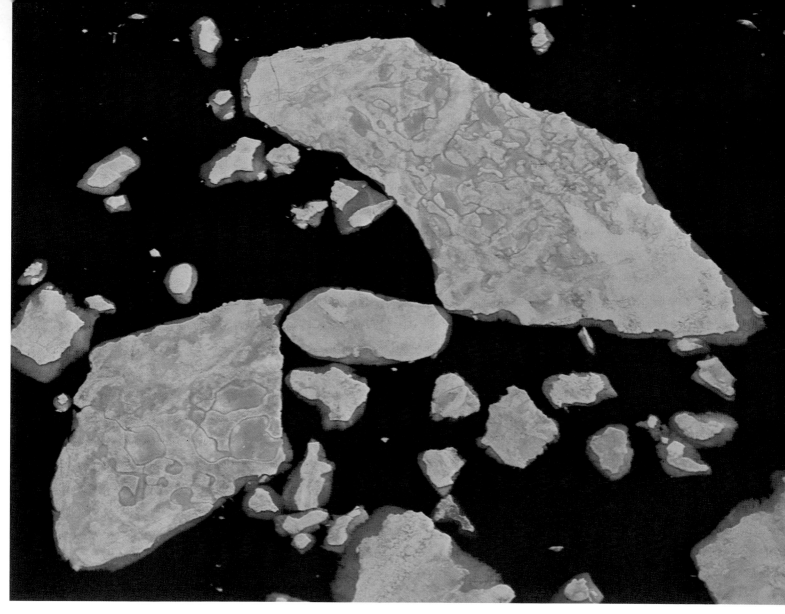

The maps at the top of page 20 show the distribution of sea ice off Iceland month by month in the years 1960-69. These charts were made by Hlynur Sigtryggsson, Director of the Icelandic Meteorological Office, on the basis of ice reconnaissance during the decade in question, indicating areas where sea ice was seen at some time during each month. At the bottom of page 20 there is a graph comparing the extent of sea ice during the months of March and April in the period of 1940 to 1969, indicating the percentage of the total area of the ice charts which at some time during these months were covered by sea ice. These graphs should, therefore, afford a rough comparison of the amount of ice in different years within the area covered by the map.

The aerial view above is of ice floes with ridges of ice and puddles of water. Considerable melting by the sun takes place on the surface. The sun heats the puddles more than the drier ice ridges so that melting is more rapid in and near the puddles.

21

Sea ice has reached the shores at Hornbjarg, making navigation difficult. This picture was taken during a reconnaissance flight in snow showers on March 24 1968. Hornbjarg is a majestic mountain, not least when viewed from the sea with its precipitous cliff-face right down to the sea. To the extreme right in the picture is Horn, then Miðfell and finally Kálfatindur. The rock formation of Hornbjarg reveals the same beauty in summer and winter, but in summer the contrast between the steep and grassy slopes of Ystidalur and the sheer rock-face near by is more pronounced. But this picture was taken when sea ice and snow showers dominated the scene.

Due to regular ice-reconnaissance flights by the Icelandic Coast Guard and more exact collection of data and comprehensive records on the extent of drift ice north of Iceland during the last three and a half decades, this period is, of course, of much greater value for research and constitutes a more promising basis for ice-forecasts than older sources.

At the bottom of page 20 an attempt is made to compare the amount of sea ice near Iceland in the months of March and April for all the years of 1940 to 1969 by showing statistically the percentage of the area of the ice maps above covered by sea ice sometime during each of these months each year. The months of March and April are usually a period when the sea ice is closest to Iceland, and therefore these statistics should enable us to make a comparison of the amount of sea ice within the map area in the different years.

The sea ice in the vicinity of Iceland has now been considered at some length. It is appropriate, therefore, to look again to the north and east, to the North Atlantic and the Arctic Ocean, where most of the drift ice comes from as mentioned above. It is not likely that man's technology will ever enable him to affect this heavy stream of drift ice with the East Greenland Current along the east coast of Greenland, but knowledge of the variation of wind and current strength can be useful for an investigation of the possibility of drift ice forecasts for Iceland. Recent research has shown that wind carries ice between the current systems of the Arctic Ocean, and this variation again causes an alteration in the amount of sea ice in the East Greenland Current. As the drifting time for the sea ice from the North Polar Region to the ocean north of Iceland is about one year, it would appear that it might be possible to foresee the amount of sea ice in the East Greenland Current some time ahead, provided it is known that a continuous wind direction has caused transportation of sea ice into the transverse current over the North Pole, which is the beginning of the East Greenland Current.

But the amount of sea ice in that current at its origin is far from being a sufficient indication to make possible the forecasting of drift ice to the shores of Iceland. The movement of the drift ice is to a very great extent dominated by the climatic conditions and the sea currents between Iceland and Spitsbergen and still more so between Iceland and Jan Mayen. It is now generally accepted that continuous west and south-westerly winds over the North Greenland Sea can for longer or shorter periods stop or retard the flow of drift ice south along the east coast of Greenland. In this way the amount of sea ice will spread, and the ice coverage north of Iceland will be wider than usual.

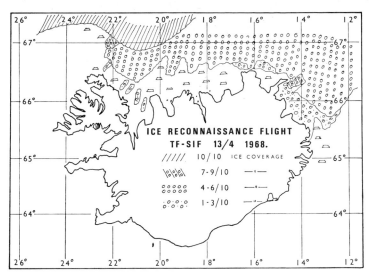

The illustration above is an ice chart based on a reconnaissance flight by TF-SIF on April 13, 1968. The estimated density of the ice is indicated on the chart. Thus, 10/10 coverage denotes that the drift ice covers the sea surface completely, whereas 1-3/10 coverage indicates that one to three tenths of the surface of the sea are covered with drift ice while nine to seven tenths are ice-free. Sometimes single floes are also shown on ice charts.

Below a convoy of ships is sailing through drift ice out of Eskifjörður on the east coast of Iceland on May 29, 1968. A coastguard vessel is in front, followed by a freighter and four fishing vessels.

The meteorological reasons might be the number and directions of passing atmospheric depressions. When the compressed masses of ice start moving again, an altered wind direction and the East Greenland Current could carry the drift ice to the Icelandic shores.

There are still many obscure factors that govern the movement of the sea ice north and east of Iceland, but the visits of sea ice during the last thirty years have increased the curiosity of scientists. Doubtless further oceanographic and meteorological research will increase our knowledge of drift ice.

In the past Icelandic poets referred to drift ice as 'Iceland´s age-old foe'. Today a number of scientists are eager to increase their knowledge of this unwelcome visitor to be in a better position to prevent its adverse influence on the economy of the Icelandic people.

Drift ice in bays and fjords (left) cools the sea and upon melting, reduces its salinity between the ice floes. Therefore, the open sea between the floes often freezes over.

To the right is an aerial view of dense drift ice north of Iceland in a low winter sun.

Above is an aerial view of Drangajökull from the sea on May 29, 1968. Sea ice is still lurking off the coast. All the three nunataks of Drangajökull, Hrolleifsborg farthest to the left, then Reyðar- bunga and Hljóðabunga, can be seen at the head of Reykjafjörður. These are three great rock castles, the biggest of which is Hrolleifs- borg, which is 851 m high. Great rock walls extend to the north, but to the south they disappear underneath the glacier.

On the right there is a view from the top of Hljóðabunga to Reyðarbunga and to the Drangajökull glacier. Maps dating from 1911-1914 show the area of Drangajökull to be approximately 200 km², but like other Icelandic glaciers it has shrunk appreciably in the last few decades and now it is approximately 165 km² in area. It is, however, still the fifth biggest glacier in Iceland. Reyðarbunga was ice-covered at the turn of the century. Then it emerged like the back of a whale, which is actually the literal meaning of its present name, given by Baldur Sveinsson, then the owner of Þara- látursfjörður.

glaciers

From the beginning of the settlement of Iceland its glaciers with their snow-white caps against the blue sky have been extolled for their majestic beauty. That is how they are referred to in many a poem, and the Icelandic nation has certainly got to know their many different facets during eleven centuries of cohabitation. It even appears that the Icelanders were in fact the first to understand the development and nature of glaciers. If the material written about glaciers in Icelandic had been published in a world language, some of the findings based on the studies of local farmers would have been considered a significant contribution to the glaciology of the time.

There is no doubt that some of the Norwegian settlers did know glaciers in their homeland, and in Iceland some of them settled very close to the glaciers. Routes between farms were from the beginning in many places along the edge of glaciers or even across glaciers. No wonder the Icelanders in time acquired some intimate understanding of this phenomenon of nature. At the time of settlement there was most likely a period of mild climate in Iceland, and therefore glaciers were then smaller than they became later on. Thus, the settler Þórður Illugi is known to have built his farm at the foot of Breiðamerkurfjall (lit. 'Breiðamerkur Mountain') between the outlet glaciers Fjalljökull and Breiðamerkurjökull about 900 A.D. (see picture on page 84), but this farm (called Fjall) was buried under a glacier during the years 1695 to 1709.

It is well known that a glacier is a mass of ice, covering mountains or valleys all the year round, the ice being formed naturally from compacted snow. It is evident that a glacier will be formed only if more snow falls during winter than is melted away during the summer. Often snow remains in valleys or depressions even though the mountain tops and ridges close by become ice-free in summer.

It has been calculated that glaciers cover 11800 km², or about 11.5% of the area of Iceland. By far the biggest of the Icelandic glaciers is the Vatnajökull, which is about 8400 km² in area. The next in size are Langjökull 1020 km², Hofsjökull 996 km², Mýrdalsjökull 700 km², Drangajökull 200 km², Eyjafjallajökull 107 km², and Tungnafellsjökull 50 km². Other glaciers in Iceland are less than 30 km² in area.

The oldest written source on Icelandic glaciers is Saxo's famous Danish History, written about 1200 A.D. It also contains a general description of Iceland which he doubtless based on Icelandic information. After having described the sea ice, Saxo writes: 'There is also another type of ice, covering areas between mountain ridges and peaks, and it is considered that this type of ice changes its position according to a certain rule, with a kind of circulating movement, so that the uppermost layer sinks down to the bottom and the lowest parts move up to the top'.

This is by far the oldest explanation of the movement of outlet glaciers, and to a certain extent it is correct as far as ice movements at their foot is concerned. Saxo also tells of people who had fallen into a crevasse and were later found dead on the surface of the glacier. This story is most likely based on actual facts as it was quite common for people living south of Vatnajökull to pass over the tongue of an outlet glacier to get from one farmstead to another.

The postman Jón Pálsson was lost on September 7, 1927. Together with his four horses he disappeared into a deep crevasse on his way over the Breiðamerkurjökull when a narrow snow bridge broke at a spot where the glacial river Jökulsá emerges from under the glacier. On April 7 the following year his body was found together with his horses on the surface of the glacier near the place where the accident occurred. 'The glacier delivers back what it takes', is an old Icelandic saying. The main reason is the rotational movement of the ice masses in an outlet glacier, a phenomenon known to the Icelanders for centuries before it was noticed by foreign glaciologists.

On a bright summer day the view along Kaldalón valley to Drangajökull is beautiful. The dark-brown glacial river Mórilla emerges from under the outlet glacier and meanders down the valley between old moraines. It is said that in 1840 the outlet glacier covered all this area and that the farm Lónhóll was destroyed by a glacier burst in 1741. In the bottom part of Kaldalón there are gravel plains and moraines with very little vegetation, but further out and on the slopes there is beautiful vegetation, grassland, heather and birch shrubbery.

Fláajökull in Suðursveit (above) is one of the outlet glaciers from the eastern part of Vatnajökull. (see map on p. 52). This is how the snouts of outlet glaciers with their gaping crevasses often look as the ice melts. The melting, however, is continuously compensated by ice advancing under the pressure of the ice cap above.

The first map in the world to show glaciers by means of special markings is the map of Iceland by Bishop Guðbrandur Þorláksson of Hólar. This map was drawn before 1585 and published in the map collection by Ortelius in 1590 (see figures on page 6 and 133). In this connection it should be mentioned that travelling across the Icelandic highlands was common in former days, and it is considered certain that fishermen even frequently crossed the Vatnajökull glacier in the 15th and 16th centuries on their way between their homes in the north and the fishing centres south of the glacier. It is well known that the subglacial volcano Grímsvötn ('Grim Lakes') on Vatnajökull (see map on page 52 and description on page 58) got its name before 1600, and only an eye-witness could have given it this name. In his glaciological treatise of 1695 the headmaster of the Skálholt School, Þórður Þorkelsson Vídalín, describes the nature of glaciers. He quite clearly got a good deal of his knowledge from people living in close proximity to glaciers. He does not always accept their views, however, although in many cases they have proved to be more correct than his own. He says people believe that in winter more snow is accumulated in the mountains than is melted in summer because the mountains are colder than the lowlands. Therefore the glaciers are subjected to heavy pressures and spread down on to the lowlands. Vídalín also tells of a two days' journey, made by a farmer named Jón Ketilsson from his farm south of Vatnajökull to its northern edge and back again. This trip was made about the middle of the 17th century and is, therefore, most likely one of the very first known explorations of a glacier.

One of the most important works on glaciology in the 19th century is the Glacier Treatise by Sveinn Pálsson (1762-1840).

Sveinn Pálsson studied medicine and natural history at the University of Copenhagen, and he wrote in Danish his Treatise on Glaciers during the years 1792-94 when he was back in Iceland, making several scientific expeditions at the same time.

This is the beginning of an ascent of Drangajökull from Kaldalón on a beautiful summer day. The view is away from the glacier over Kaldalón to Ísafjarðardjúp. If the ascent is made from Votubjörg to the south of Kaldalón the crevasses can be by-passed to a large extent. Extreme caution must be exercised, however, as always on glaciers because crevasses may be covered with freshly fallen snow. More dangerous still are the glacier pot-holes, which are funnel-shaped water channels in the glacier ice.

His work remained unpublished and completely forgotten until part of it was published in 1882, but it was not published in full until 1945, when it was translated into Icelandic by Jón Eyþórsson, forming part of his work 'The Travels of Sveinn Pálsson'.

In his work Sveinn Pálsson puts forward the theory that glaciers move like a plastic mass. This he based on his own observations of the Breiðamerkurjökull Glacier in 1793, and he became convinced that this theory was correct when he was the first to climb the Öræfajökull on August 11 1794. In his diary Sveinn Pálsson writes on his ascent of this glacier: 'My attention was mainly drawn to the outlet glacier mentioned above, which moves downwards just east of the farm Kvísker. The surface of this glacier was covered with circular stripes across it, especially near the glacier, and these ogives were bent towards the lowland, indicating that this outlet glacier was actually flowing in a half-melted state like a thick plastic mass. Would this not indicate, in fact, that the ice by its very nature is semi-liquid and flows-without melting-like some types of harpix as I mentioned in the last chapter?'.

Quite clearly Sveinn Pálsson did not know that the Frenchman A.C. Bordiers had already 20 years earlier published a paper, in which he advanced similar ideas, viz. that glaciers move like a plastic mass. This glaciological work by Sveinn Pálsson stands out as an achievement of a high order as well as the central point of a glaciology which may be looked upon as specifically Icelandic since it was based on the experience of Icelanders of Icelandic glaciers.

Simultaneously and independently glaciology was developed in the Alpine region, which later became the basis of the international glaciology of today. For a time Icelandic glaciology even led the way, but it was later completely forgotten until a few decades ago when Iceland again became a centre of interest for glaciologists.

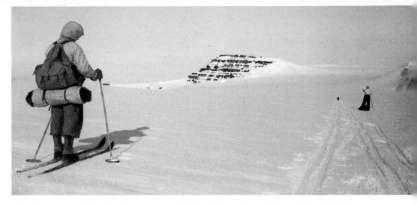

On Drangajökull glacier on Whit-Sunday, June 5 1938. - Hrolleifsborg is straight ahead, but to the right is Reyðarbunga, covered with snow. The picture below was taken on the same spot on August 21 1966. Hrolleifsborg is to the left and Reyðarbunga to the right. The glacier has quite clearly shrunk during the intervening 28 years, even though it must be taken into account that the older picture was taken earlier in the year.

An overnight camp on Hrolleifsborg on Drangajökull at a height of 851 m (right). Reyðarbunga and the ice-cap of Drangajökull (925 m) are in the background.

outlet glaciers

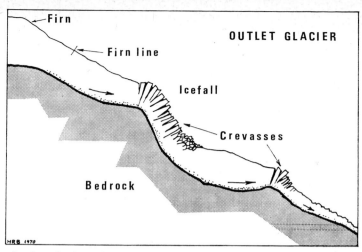

It is known that a glacier is formed in places where the annual snowfall exceeds the amount of snow and ice that is lost by melting during the warm season. The snow that falls on an ice cap changes gradually. Most of the snow falls during winter when one layer after another is formed.

The accumulation of snow, however, varies with temperature and weather conditions. When the snow melts and freezes again, especially during spring and autumn, ice layers commonly appear between the snow layers. When it rains or the snow is melting, melt-water flows into the lower layers and alters their structure. The snow crystals increase in size, assuming ice-like properties, partly due to the pressure from the snow above. In this way the snow gradually turns into firn.

This is explained in greater detail on page 66. A snow pit dug on an ice cap like Bárðarbunga or Öræfajökull (see map on page 52) will readily show up the ice layers and illustrate how glacier ice is transformed into firn. Finally, there are coarse layers of snow, often in conjunction with more dense ice layers. These are layers from the previous summer and autumn, and if the pit is dug near the edge of the glacier, layers of sand or dust, carried up to the glacier by the wind during summer or autumn, may also be found.

But why do not glaciers grow higher each year since a 4 to 8 metre thick snow layer may be added on to the ice cap in one year? Here we come to the crux of glaciology. As Sveinn Pálsson discovered and explained quite correctly in his glaciological work of the 18th century, the reason is that although ice is hard and fragile, it has a considerable plasticity like harpix or pitch. Glacier ice is softer than a layer of sea ice, and therefore glacier ice moves slowly under the pressure of its own ice caps from the mountains down through valleys below the firn-line, where the temperature is higher and melting is more rapid than in the highlands.

Outlet glaciers drain the ice caps, the pressure of which pushes the ice down to lower levels where it melts until an equilibrium at the snout is reached between melting and the advance of the ice. Crevasses develop where the ice passes over uneven bedrock, making passage difficult and necessitating crampons, ice-axes and ropes.

The picture on the right shows the glacial waters of the river Morilla as seen from Votubjörg to the south of Kaldalón. Their dark-brown colour contrasts sharply with the clear-blue puddles in hollows between old moraines of the outlet glacier. Green vegetation and the barren desert, contrasts of Icelandic nature, meet here, providing a magnificent camping-site.

33

These are crevasses in the outlet glacier of Langjökull where it extends its snout into Lake Hvítárvatn. Langjökull is the second biggest glacier in Iceland, its size being 1020 km² as measured on maps of 1939. At the present time it is somewhat smaller.

In the last few decades Langjökull has created the so-called jökulborgir ('glacier castles') above Lake Hagavatn. These huge ice edifices (picture on the right) are apparently formed when a moving ice cover passes over uneven bedrock.

34

Air temperature falls by about 0.5-0.7° C on the average for every 100 metres we go up in altitude above sea level. Hence there is often snowfall in the mountains when it is raining in the lowlands.

Each area has an equilibrium at a certain altitude above sea level. Above that altitude snow will accumulate year after year, forming a glacier, but below that same altitude the winter snow will melt away during summer. This yearly melting-limit is called 'snow line', whereas its mean altitude over a period of some years is called firn line.

The firn line lies at very different heights in Iceland. For example, at the southern edge of Vatnajökull the firn line is 1000 to 1100 m above sea level, but at the northern edge of that same glacier the firn line is at an altitude of 1200 to 1400 m as the north side is sheltered from the wettest wind direction. On Drangajökull in the Vestfirðir area (the North West) the firn line usually lies at an altitude of 600-700 m.

It is noteworthy, incidentally, that the term *skriðjökull* ('a creeping glacier') was originally only to be found in the Icelandic language, indicating that the Icelanders have for a long time known the nature of outlet glaciers, which move or slide down under pressure of the ice masses draining the ice caps, which in turn, slowly sink as the ice masses below glide down towards the lowlands.

An ice cap, therefore, does not increase its height if the climate remains constant, even though more snow is accumulated there every year than the warm season can melt away. Further down the outlet glacier more and more of the ice is melted and at its front the movement and the melting is balanced. This equilbrium, however, can be disturbed. If some years of unusually heavy snowfall are followed by cold summers, an outlet glacier may advance further down the valley or on to the lowlands before an equilibrium is reached again. Conversely, the snout of an outlet glacier will retreat if several years of relatively light snowfall are followed by warm summers, and that has been the case of Icelandic outlet glaciers during the last few decades.

The above picture is of the Sólheimajökull outlet glacier snout where an equilibrium has been reached between advance and melting. Below is the Gígjökull outlet of Eyjafjallajökull glacier where it extends down into a small glacier lake.

In Karlsdráttur (left) at the end of Lake Hvítárvatn there is beautiful vegetation just by the snout of the Langjökull outlet glacier. Mt. Skriðufell is in the background. A few decades ago it was entirely enclosed by outlet glaciers. The maximum depth of Lake Hvítárvatn is 70 m off Mt. Skriðufell.

Although the Langjökull outlet glacier at Hvítárvatn is not of the same dimensions as it used to be, it is still quite impressive at close quarters. Many fantastic ice formations appear in the churned-up ice masses.

Many of the crevasses in the Langjökull outlet glacier are of immense proportions (photograph right). Slowly the ice makes its way down to Lake Hvítárvatn. No movement can be discerned by people walking on the outlet glacier, but now and then there are big thuds and bangs.

Above is a view from Norðurjökull, outlet glacier of Langjökull, over Lake Hvítárvatn to Kerlingarfjöll. Karlsdráttur is to the left.

To the south of Arnarfell hið mikla an outlet glacier extends from Hofsjökull down to Þjórsárver. This outlet glacier dams up a glacier lake which is filled with water in early spring. Ice floes break off the outlet glacier and float on the lake until it is empty in early summer. The remaining floes (right) then often make up the most grotesque ice formations.

The picture above is a view over the river Þjórsá and Þjórsárver to Hofsjökull and Arnarfell. Arnarfellsjökull is a beautifully shaped glacier which extends from Hofsjökull down to Þjórsárver, which is a continuous grass-covered area at the south-eastern edge of Hofsjökull. Þjórsárver is to some extent a tundra because the subsoil is often frozen all summer. This area is the world's biggest colony of the pink-footed goose with at least 9000 pairs nesting there.

Below is a view of Mýrdalsjökull where Katla, one of the most active volcanoes of Iceland, rests under the ice sheet. Katla eruptions produce enormous glacier floods. Katla is apparently situated on a volcanic fissure which is most likely an extension of the Eldgjá fissure. The last Katla eruption occurred in 1918.

When outlet glaciers retreat, as they have been doing in Iceland for the last 60-70 years, they cause a great deal of alteration to the surrounding landscape. At Lake Hagavatn and in the Jarlhettudalur valley at the edge of Langjökull glacier the landscape has, for example, undergone a radical change. Big pieces of ice may remain for some time buried in clay and sand where the glacier has withdrawn, and walking may be difficult in knee-deep mud on the top of a layer of dead ice, preventing the water from getting away. But vegetation reaches this new area surprisingly quickly, even if there is still ice underneath. In mid-summer the vegetation is often so soggy that a man walking in it penetrates to the ice layer.

Gígjökull (right) in the northern part of Eyjafjallajökull goes down to a small glacier lake, wich is sometimes dotted with ice floes from the outlet glacier.

Snæfellsjökull

Snæfellsjökull is the name of the 1446 m high fascinating ice cap at the extreme end of the Snæfellsnes Peninsula.

Even in Reykjavik, 115 km away, this regularly shaped volcanic cone with its snow cap on top makes a grand spectacle. In mid-summer the sunsetting behind the golden cap of SnæfeIlsjökull throws an almost indescribale array of colours over the Faxaflói Bay. On a map of 1910 the glacier is shown to be about 22 km², but its size has shrunk rapidly during the last half century, being now little more than 11 km².

After a warm summer long mountain ridges to the south are often free of ice. There has been no volcanic eruption in Snæfellsjökull in historical time, but volcanic craters can be easily seen. The top crater is the biggest one, but it is completely covered by the glacier, not a single stone being visible in the caldera. The edges of the crater, on the other hand, are prominent landmarks because three singIe rocks, which are parts of the crater edge, are actually very characteristic features of the mountain. In winter and spring they are usually ice-covered, but during summer and autumn the black rocks become visible. Lava must have flowed in all directions down the slopes of the mountain, and around it there are several old craters which at one time discharged lava streams that extended all the way down to the sea.

It is quite easy to climb Snæfellsjökull at any time of the year. In early spring the snow reaches further down the slopes than at other times, necessitating a longer trek in the snow. Four to five hours should be allowed for walking from the lowland to the highest peak from the south-west side. The route has very few crevasses in the spring as can be seen in the picture on this page, but when the peak is covered with ice as it is in these pictures, good crampons are essential. An ice axe and a nylon rope are also recommended, although the crevasses are usually not much open in the spring.

Above is a view of Snæfellsjökull from the south-east. From the lowlands it certainly makes a majestic spectacle that is a lure to would-be climbers on a fine day. The picture was taken on May 2, the snow reaching much farther down the slopes than later in the summer.

Below is a view to the north from the highest peak of Snæfellsjökull. Breiðafjörður is in the background.

At the highest peak of Snæfellsjökull on May 1, 1967 (left). Snæfellsjökull is an extinct volcano, 1446 m. in height. At the mountain top there are three peaks, two of them precipitous rocks, black in summer and covered with a glassy ice mantle in winter and in spring. Here is a view of the caldera, covered with glacier ice.

47

A Vatnajökull expedition at the foot of Grímsfjall at the side of the Grímsvötn depression, - a volcanic area under the ice of central Vatnajökull. During volcanic eruptions a hole is sometimes melted in the ice sheet above, as can be seen in the picture on p.189 of the Grímsvötn eruption of 1983.

Above, a train of snowmobiles is near the edge of the Tungnaárjökull glacier at the beginning of a Vatnajökull expedition. It is often quite hard to get snowmobiles and luggage to the edge of the glacier because of glacial rivers and mud. Sledges, towed by snowmobiles, are loaded with equipment, provisions and barrels of fuel.

Below, the train of snowmobiles has reached a mast erected for snow measurements on Vatnajökull. A pit is dug in the ice to measure the thickness of the snow layer that has accumulated in the preceding year and to take samples of the glacier ice at various depths. In the background is the nunatak Pálsfjall.

On Öræfajökull. Below is a view from Jökulbak (1922 m) to Hvannadalshnjúkur. the highest peak in Iceland, 2119 m. The snowmobile route from the wide expanses of Vatnajökull to Öræfajökull is along the ridge of the pass of Hermannaskarð, past Þuríðartindur, along the ridge at the pass of Tjaldskarð, on to Snæbreið (2041 m) and from there to the foot of Hvannadalshnjúkur, which towers almost 250 m above the glacial plain (see map on p. 52).

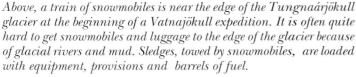

Vatnajökull

Vatnajökull is by far the biggest glacier in Iceland. Maps of the years 1904 to 1938 indicate its area to be about 8400 km², and although it has shrunk somewhat during the last few decades, it is still almost as big as all the glaciers on the European Continent combined. During the French-Icelandic Vatnajökull Expedition in 1951 the thickness of the ice was measured by means of echo-sounding equipment. Then it was found that the ice is much thicker than was commonly believed before. The measurements showed the thickness of the ice in general to be 600-800 m. and the greatest ice thickness measured was 1000 m.

The main part of Vatnajökull, therefore, rests on a mountainous landscape, made up of valleys and mountain ridges no more than 800-1000 m above sea level. As mentioned before, the firn line at the southern edge of Vatnajökull is at an altitude of 1100 m. Therefore, if the ice cap suddenly melted away, no glacier would be formed again in this area, except for small ice caps on the highest peaks, provided the climate remained the same as it has been during the last 60-70 years. The measurements also indicated quite clearly that in many valleys which are now covered by thick ice there might after some time be fertile farmland.

But as the situation is now, the surface of the Vatnajökull glacier is mostly at an altitude of 1400-1600 m above sea level, and therefore this glacial area continues to collect winter snow since it extends well above the firn line. Thus, the greater part of Vatnajökull is a fairly even ice cap or ice sheet, although there are some slight bulges and depressions. The highest ice cap, Bárðarbunga, which is about 2000 m high, is on the north-west part of the ice sheet, its slopes at the western extremity of the glacier being almost precipitous.

In many places the Vatnajökull ice sheet is encircled by border mountains, some of them having peaks reaching high above the main ice sheet and therefore greatly enhancing the majestic view of the glacier.

Among these border mountains are Kerlingar (1339 m) and Hamarinn (1573 m) to the west, Kverkfjöll (1920 m) to the north, and Hrútfjallstindar (1875 m) and Miðfellstindur (1430 m) to the south. The Öræfajökull ice cap is, in a way, a separate glacier as it is on a much higher level, although it is connected to the main ice sheet of Vatnajökull. Rising out of the main ice sheet of Vatnajökull, there are also some nunataks, single mountains and ridges surrounded by ice, such as Pálsfjall (1335 m) and Grímsfjall (1725 m) in the western part of the Vatnajökull ice sheet, Grendill (1570 m) to the east, Esjufjöll (1522 m) and Máfabyggðir (1449 m) in the southern part, near Breiðamerkurjökull. On the Öræfajökull ice cap there are the nunataks Þuríðartindur (1741 m) to the north-east, Knappar (1758-2044 m) to the east and south, and finally the Hvannadalshnjúkur to the north-west, 2119 m, the highest peak in Iceland.

A look at a map of Vatnajökull (see page 52) makes it clear how the outlet glaciers flow out from the ice sheet down to the lowlands wherever the border mountains do not prevent their movement until a balance is reached between the accumulation of snow above the firn line and the flow and melting of the outlet glaciers. Crevasses occur in greatest numbers where an outlet glacier has a high speed, but they are also common high up on the ice sheet above the outlets.

Until about 25 years ago the biggest obstacle in the way of Vatnajökull expeditions from inhabited areas to Jökulheimar, the hut of the Iceland Glaciological Society at the foot of Tungnaárjökull glacier, was the river Tungnaá. Below, a train of vehicles is crossing the Tungnaá on the Hofsvað ford. Now this river has been bridged further down.

Often the best way to climb the glacier, therefore, is to follow a border mountain or a mountain ridge reaching into the interior. Along the western edge of Vatnajökull the outlet glaciers are almost continuous and are only divided by single mountains. These glaciers are called after the rivers issuing from them: Köldukvíslarjökull, Tungnaárjökull, Skaftárjökull, and Síðujökull.

Along the southern edge there are many border mountains, keeping the glacier closed in so that the outlet glaciers here mostly flow down valleys. The biggest outlet glaciers along the southern edge are Skeiðarárjökull and Breiðamerkurjökull, but some smaller, though very steep, outlet glaciers extend from the Öræfajökull. From the Breiðabunga area there are Hoffellsjökull, Fláajökull, and Heinabergsjökull. The biggest outlet glaciers extending from the northern edge of Vatnajökull are the Brúarjökull and Dyngjujökull and, finally, Kverkjökull, a small valley glacier coming out of Kverkin, a part of an old volcanic crater in Kverkfjöll (see picture on page 107).

These Vatnajökull outlet glaciers are not alike. They behave very differently, each of them actually requiring a separate study although they have some characteristics in common. Some of them, such as the Skeiðarárjökull, dam up lakes in side-valleys.

Such lakes cause *jökulhlaup* ('glacier floods') when the water is emptied at intervals of some years (see further on page 84-87). The nature of each outlet glacier is, of course, greatly influenced by its surroundings, e.g. the landscape under the glacier, the size and altitude of the ice cap from which it extends, whether mountains limit the width of a valley glacier, and finally, what is of importance for all outlet glaciers, the yearly accumulation of snow above the firn line and the melting below it. The glaciers are slow in their reaction to climatic changes, and therefore such changes have to last for many years before their effects on the glacier become evident.

However, big and flat outlet glaciers seem to be more sensitive to irregular climatic variations than thick and

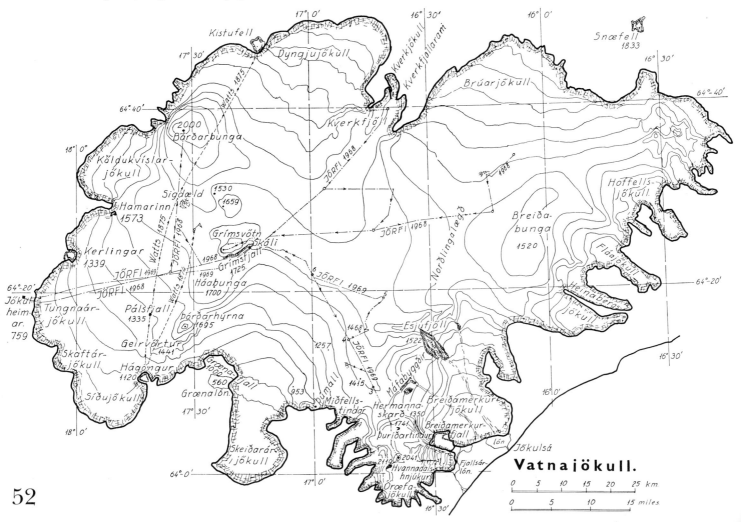

Vatnajökull.

narrow valley glaciers, confined by mountains on both sides. So far, no theory has been advanced to explain the sudden and often completely unexpected advance of these big and flat outlet glaciers of Vatnajökull. The reason might possibly be a reluctance on the part of the outlet glacier to increase its moving speed evenly due to a frictional resistance of the ground layers even though increased ice masses on the main glacier require an increased speed of the outlet to maintain an equilibrium. Due to the slow movement of the outlet glacier melting would decrease its thickness higher up than usual. This process might continue until the thin outlet glacier was getting too light to withstand the increasing pressure from the thicker glacier higher up, when it would cause a sudden advance of the outlet glacier which then would move further down than would have been the case if the accumulation of snow each year had been balanced by movement and melting.

This is only a guess, but Vatnajökull is very suitable for a study of the behaviour of this type of outlet glaciers. In point of fact, Brúarjökull suddenly advanced in the winter of 1963-64 up to 8 km. It is also known that Brúarjökull advanced similarly in 1890. In a Vatnajökull expedition in the summer of 1966 a snowmobile partly fell into a crevasse on the route between Grímsfjöll and Kverkfjöll. The crevasses from the advance of Brúarjökull in 1963-64 were reaching that far, and members of the summer expedition of the Iceland Glaciological Society in 1968 found that there were still crevasses a long way into the glacier as shown on the map on page 52 .

Regular measurements of variations in the outlet glaciers of Vatnajökull started in 1930. They only cover the southern glaciers, however, and during the last 25 years also Tungnaárjökull. On the other hand, the outlet glaciers which are shown to have advanced suddenly are all of the big and flat type, mainly in the north and west parts of Vatnajökull. Besides Brúarjökull, the following have had sudden advances: Síðujökull in 1934 and again in 1963-64. The last advance was studied from the air and crevasses and movement were noticed up above Pálsfjall. Skaftárjökull advanced in 1945. Both Dyngjujökull and Síðujökull advanced in 1934, and Síðujökull again in 1951. The total areas of Vatnajökull which have advanced or moved suddenly since 1930, including the advance of 1890, amount to about 40% of the total area of Vatnajökull.

It is believed that fishermen from the north did not cross Vatnajökull after 1575. Someone must have been to the Grímsvötn caldera as mentioned before because this name is very old. However, the crossing of Vatnajökull was apparently not very common in former days and the oldest maps of Iceland indicate that people were entirely unaware of the enormous size of the Vatnajökull area. Therefore, the

south-east part of the country used to appear unduly slim on early maps. The northern and southern edges of the Vatnajökull glacier were known, but not the very substantial distance between them.

It is not until 1875 that written sources relate of a crossing of Vatnajökull. It was made by a Scottish explorer, W.L.Watts, together with some Icelandic guides. It is clear that Watts principally relied on Páll Pálsson, and he named the nunatak Pálsfjall after his guide, not himself. Watt and his companions tried to cross Vatnajökull in 1874, but had to give it up due to bad weather. In 1875 they went all the way in 12 days. The estimated route of Watt and his company is shown on the map on page 52. Most likely they would not have had to take a route much farther to the east to find the Grímsvötn caldera, which then were only known by an old tradition.

The next crossing of Vatnajökull was made by two Scots on skis. They spent 22 days on the glacier. A Danish surveyor, J. P. Koch, crossed Vatnajökull with four guides on Icelandic horses in 1912. They came from the north, went to Esjufjöll and back again. This was part of a preparation for an expedition across the Greenland ice sheet in 1912-13, using Icelandic horses. A member of this expedition was the Icelander, Vigfús Guðmundsson, subsequently called Vigfús the Greenland-traveller.

To be towed by a snowmobile across the expanses of Vatnajökull is effortless, but exhilarating, for a skier. Nowhere is the sunlight brighter or the air fresher.

An excellent long ski-slope extends from the huts of the Iceland Glaciological Society down to Grímsvötn, but sometimes crevasses near the top have to be avoided. The light is reminiscent of the so-called whiteout exemplified by the fusion of the sky and the glacier which eliminates any visible horizon. Although there is no real fog here, it would be hard to estimate any distances if it were not for the skiers seen in the distance. - Below, men are standing near Gríðarhorn in the Grímsvötn depression. Hot springs at the foot of the mountain melt the ice, forming deep crevasses from which hot vapours stream out, cutting right through the ice layers above.

The subglacial landscape below a glacier is of great interest. The direction in which thaw water runs from a glacier is mainly determined by the declivity of the bedrock underneath, although the pressure exerted by the ice at the base of the glacier also has an influence. The surface declivity of the glacier has no significant effect on dividing the watershed that lies underneath it, but for the operation of hydroelectric power stations it has been important to measure the rate of flow. Investigations conducted by the University of Iceland Research Institute on bedrock beneath glaciers in Iceland are therefore of significant value. The University Research Institute has designed an automatic measuring instrument, known as an 'icescope' which records the hight of sub-glacial rock when it is run along the surface of the glacier. This has already made it possible to draw a contour-line map of bedrock underneath parts of Vatnajökull.

Volcanic eruptions may take place in some of the valleys or mountains covered by ice where considerable amounts of lava or tephra may come up to the surtface without breaking through the ice cap above.

A geographic comparision of Grímsvötn with other volcanic areas near the glacier shows that the Grímsvötn area is on a line connecting the Kverkfjöll and Laki. In recent years an ice cauldron ('*sigdæld*') has developed north-west of Grímsvötn (see map on p.52). It is considered likely that a subglacial eruption took place there in 1955 and also later in view of the increased amount of water in, and sulphur smell from, the glacial river Skaftá, the water outlet from this area.

Below Gríðarhorn (right) there is no need to dig pits to study a profile of the Grímsvötn ice layers because the heat cuts right through the firn. The thickness of the ice cover can be estimated from the height of the man in the picture.

research

Glacier research has a multiple purpose, one of the main objects being to study the changes glaciers undergo, their advances or retreats, including the movement of outlet glaciers.

Further, the annual ice layers in glaciers can give information on the climate of long ago, and the discovery of an ash layer from a known volcanic eruption is of very great importance for the confirmation of the age determination of ice layers.

Glaciological research actually started in 1919 with the trip of the Swedes, Wadell and Ygberg, mentioned above. Several trips were made onto Vatnajökull in the years 1934-1936 on the occasion of the Grímsvötn eruption of 1934. After the foundation of the Iceland Glaciological Society in 1950 the number of trips to Vatnajökull with mechanically driven equipment increased, both for research and for sightseeing purposes.

On the map on page 52 the routes of the Society's research expeditions in 1968 and 1969 are shown (JÖRFI 1968, 1969). Grímsvötn are visited every year for measurements, but other routes differ somewhat from year to year.

At several places in the Vatnajökull glacier snow pits are dug in the spring down through the layer of snow which has accumulated on that spot during the previous winter. Samples are taken in 30 cm long hollow cylinders from the surface of the pit to the bottom. The snow of each sample is weighed, studied and measured, and part of it is put into plastic containers for subsequent analysis in a laboratory.

From the bottom of the snow pit a hand drill is applied for a further penetration into the glacier down to a depth of about 10 m, cores of 40 cm length being taken at a time. These cores are also weighed, its ice layers studied and measured, and samples put into separate containers destined for the laboratory.

In recent years drillings have been made by means of an electrical thermal drill to collect samples from greater depths at Bárðarbunga, where a depth of more than 100 m has been reached.

The main purpose of this research work is to study the amount of snow accumulated at various points on the glacier and to determine the amount of its potential melt-water content. This knowledge is of practical value as it indicates the amount of water which can be expected to emerge from the glacier to different rivers, some of which produce electricity in hydro-electric power plants. During recent years the Science Institute of the University of Iceland has, in co-operation with the Glaciological Society, collected samples

This 8 m deep ice pit was dug on Öræfajökull at a height of 2041 m on May 27-29, 1969. Then a hand-drill was used to extract ice cores further down from its bottom for the purpose of analysis. Continuous samples are taken in metal cylinders from top to the bottom of the pit wall.

of snow from different glaciers in Iceland for the measurement of its deuterium and tritium content.

This research has shown that Bárðarbunga (2000 m) can for all practical purposes be considered an arctic glacier in the sense that very little melting takes place there in spite of its being considered a temperate glacier. Therefore, deuterium measurements of ice cores from Bárðarbunga could give information about the climate in Iceland over a period of several centuries.

Due to the pressure from the ice masses above, the lower layers are more and more compacted and are therefore thinner. Thus, the bottom ice layers in Bárðarbunga might be 400-1000 years old. It is hoped that deeper drillings there might give information on temperatures in Iceland in the past, possibly back to the time of the settlement.

A core drilling through the Greenland ice sheet was completed recently. The bottom part of the core was found to be more than 100,000 years old, and measurements of annual mean temperatures, therefore, cover the same period. These measurements are easier to make on an arctic glacier as almost no melting takes place there.

On Icelandic glaciers it is only in winter that the precipitation is in the form of snow. During summer it is mostly rain which flows away together with the part of the winter snow that is melted during the warm season.

It is easy enough to keep warm in a snow pit when drilling manually. The temperature of the snow in a pit like the one on the right is usually 0°C. near the top, but often it is -1°C to -3°C at a depth of 4-5 m. - But glaciological research also requires many other odd jobs: When staying in a camp for a while, travellers on glaciers often build toilettes of snow for their convenience (below). - Maintenance of the snowmobiles may require considerable skill (bottom right).

glacier tracks

The first explorers of Vatnajökull travelled on foot or on skis, sometimes pulling sledges. Above and below skiers are travelling in the Grímsvötn area because skis are still handy for short explorations although most tours of Vatnajökull today are made by means of snowmobiles or motor sledges. Crevasses are often found at the foot of the mountains in the Grímsvötn depression, but they are most pronounced, of course, just after a glacier flood has occurred, sinking the water level of the lake by as much as 200 m.

In former days travelling over the Icelandic glaciers was either done on foot or on horseback. In addition to crossings by fishermen over Vatnajökull from the north to the fishing stations in the Hornafjörður district, it is also known that the Drangajökull was frequently crossed when the northernmost part of the Western Fjords (Vestfirðir) was still inhabited. Then driftwood was transported across the glacier to the Ísafjarðardjúp.

The British explorer, Watts, and his Icelandic guides travelled on foot on Vatnajökull both in 1874 and 1875, pulling a sledge part of the way. The Dane, Kock, crossed Vatnajökull on horseback in 1912, and the Swedes, Wadell and Ygberg, were also on horseback when they reached Grímsvötn in 1919.

The expeditions to the volcanic eruption site at Grímsvötn in 1934-1936 were largely made on skis and sledges. The members of the Swedish-Icelandic expedition to Vatnajökull in 1936 used four sledge dogs, the only time dogs have been used for pulling sledges on Icelandic glaciers.

Today snowmobiles and motor sledges are practically the only means of transportation used on Vatnajökull expeditions, serving the dual purpose of carrying the explorers and pulling special sledges loaded with fuel barrels, provisions and equipment. Most of the participants bring with them skiing equipment, which is convenient for shorter trips. To be towed by a snowmobile over the immense expanses of Vatnajökull Glacier makes for an effortless, but exhilarating, skiing experience.

Melt-water and soft ice can make the first lap below the firn line quite difficult. On the glacier night driving is the rule when the weather is warm because then a crust of sufficient strength may be formed on the surface for the snowmobiles to ride on with relative ease. Helicopters and small conventional aircraft have been used for short visits to the glaciers.

Snowmobile tracks are seen from the Grímsfjall down to the Grímsvötn depression in the picture on the right. The first rays of the morning sun reveal any uneven features on the surface of the firn.

64

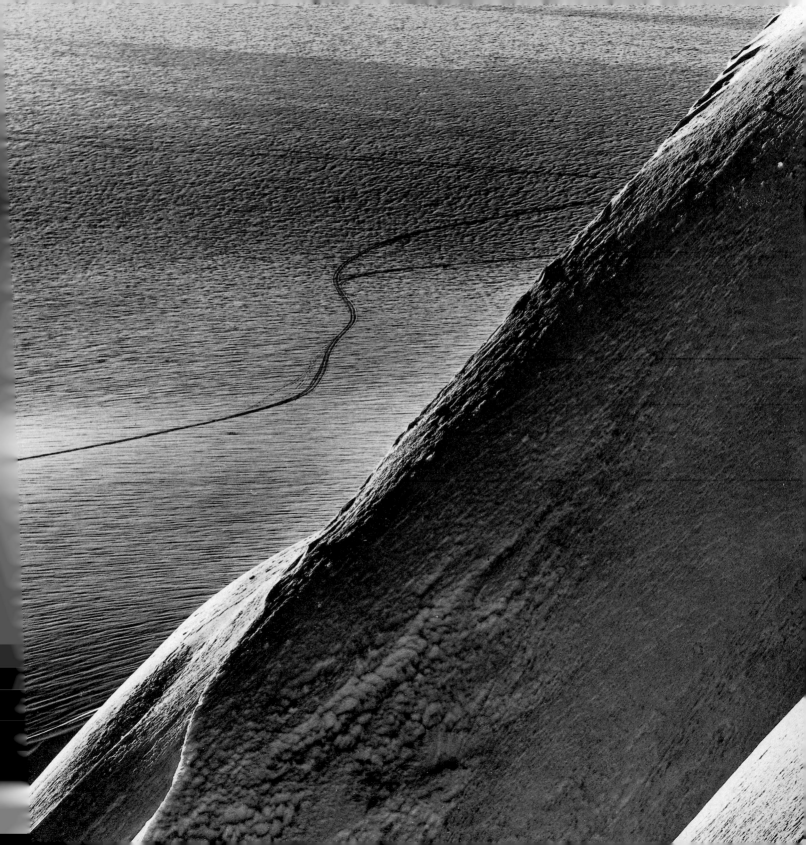

snow into ice

All fresh snow that falls on a glacier, regardless whether it falls as snowflakes or hail, gradually turns into ice. Fresh snow is very light because it contains a lot of air. All snowflakes are made up of hexagonal crystals, but they may vary a great deal in form. Sometimes the arms are formed by a network of long fine needles of ice only, but sometimes they consist of hexagonal flat plates (see picture on the left, top).

When fresh snow falls on a glacier in calm weather, a light surface layer will soon be formed. When the snow begins to drift, the arms of the snowflakes soon break off, melting slightly because of friction and any incidental sunshine. During the night they will often refreeze in their own melt-water, giving the snow a harder and more granular texture than fresh snow has (see picture middle left). This surface layer, however, still contains air cavities.

When new layers of snow accumulate on top of existing ones, their weight contribute to increased pressure. Meltwater and rain seep down into the lower layers, soon turning into ice in this frosty environment. In this way the snow is compacted by pressure, melting and refreezing into nará, granulated firn, frequently sandwiched by ice layers (see the bottom picture on the left).

Deeper down in the glacier the ice increasingly turns into compact ice with greater transparency, but still containing some air bubbles. The picture on the right shows an ice core from a depth of 40 metres on Bárðarbunga, its size having been enlarged by nearly 5 to 1. There are still several air bubbles left in spite of the great pressure above.

In the ice caves of Grímsfjall old layers of glacial ice can be seen without going to the trouble of drilling. These caves have come into being through volcanic heat melting the ice on the slope of the mountain. The bluish hues of the daylight shining through the ceiling give an eery beauty to this freak of nature (see pp.68 and 69).

The pictures on this page were all taken with macro lens equipment on June 1-2, 1969 near snow pit No. 5 north-west of Esjufjöll. It had been snowing during the night but the frost was only -5°C. Therefore the photographer had to take prompt action before the individual ice crystals melted or evaporated. The ice crystal in the top picture is about 70 times its natural size. The picture of freshly fallen snow (centre) has been enlarged about 10 times, and the same applies to the bottom picture, featuring rough firn from a drill-hole through a two-year old ice layer.

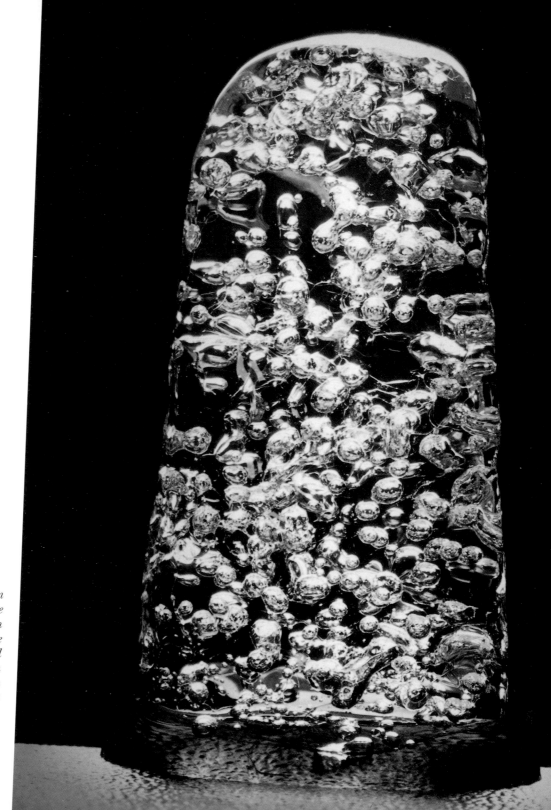

An ice core, enlarged 5 times, from a 40 m deep hole drilled in the Bárðarbunga in Vatnajökull on June 6, 1968. The ice has become glassy under pressure, but it still contains many air cavities. In 1969 a depth of more than 100 m was reached at Bárðarbunga by means of a thermal drill. At a depth of 101 m an ash layer from the 1918 eruption of Katla was found.

Under the firn covering the slopes of Grímsfjall large ice caves are formed by geothermal heat in the sides of the caldera. The entrances to the ice caves, however, are often hidden under a snow cover until the middle of summer. It is pitch-dark down there so that lighting equipment is essential. The tuff slope below is very steep and is luke-warm in places. Where daylight penetrates through crevasses in the dome the ice assumes a beautiful blue hue.

68

ice surface

The surface of glacier ice may vary enormously because the action of frost, sunshine and wind reshape the snow and the firn on the ice cap in many different ways.

The top picture on the left shows an ice surface on the eastern part of the Vatnajökull ice cap. This type of crust with ripples formed by the sun and the wind covered a wide area.

The lower picture on the left was taken of an ice cover on the very steep sides of the Hvannadalshnjúkur peak. These ice tops are mostly formed by the sun melting the surface and its refreezing.

Below is a picture from the thermal ice caves of Grímsfjall where the volcanic heat has unevenly melted the various layers of the ice.

The picture on the right was taken in drifting snow. The sharp irregular ridges formed by wind erosion and deposition are called *sastrugi*. They run parallel to the direction of the wind.

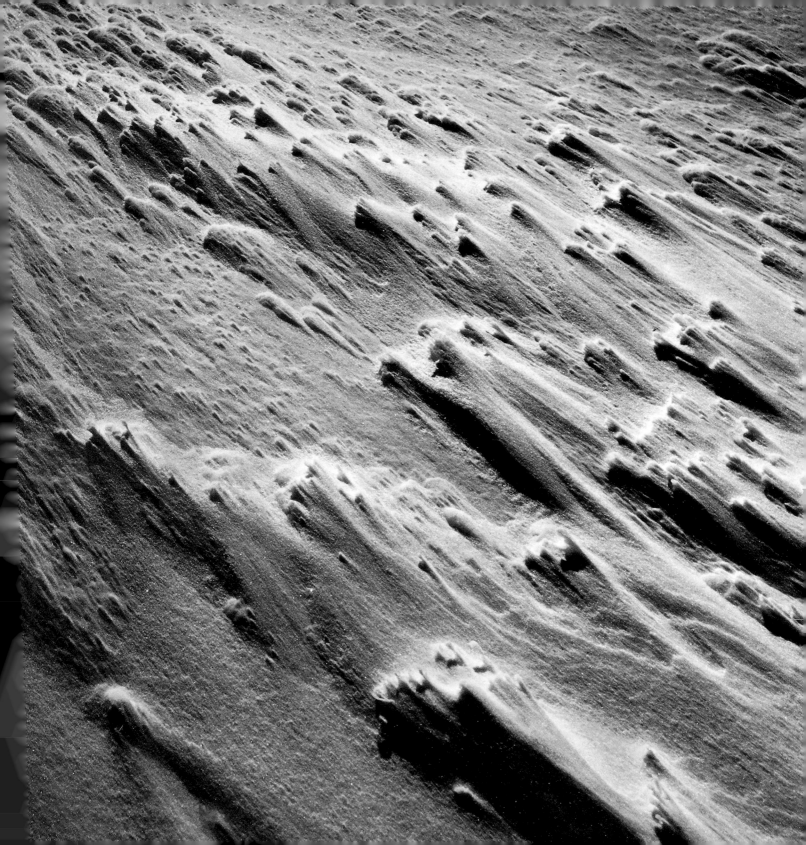

Sunrise on the glacial firn (left) is a breathtaking spectacle: The roseate colours of dawn blend with the bluish hues of the firn in a magnificent ever-changing display. This picture was taken on the eastern part of Vatnajökull on June 11, 1968.

Above is a view towards Herðubreið from the eastern part of Vatnajökull, facing Brúarjökull. Circuitous snowmobile tracks are evidence of the frequent necessity to bypass crevasses.

Öræfajökull

Although Öræfajökull is connected to the main ice sheet of Vatnajökull, it is really a separate ice cap because it lies on a considerably higher level south of the main glacier. They are connected by an ice ridge, Hermannaskarð (1350 m), on the west side of the nunatak Þuríðartindur (1741 m), and a separate ice cap called Jökulbak (1922 m), which offers an excellent view of Hvannadalshnjúkur (2119 m), the highest peak in Iceland, towering majestically with its ice cover usually right to the top. Then there is Tjaldskarð (1844 m), a narrow snow-covered pass which must be negotiated with great care because both sides are very steep. Then there is another ice cupola, Snæbreið (2041 m). From its top there is a magnificent view of the enormous ice-filled caldera of the volcano, Öræfajökull. Many peaks along the edges tower above the ice cover, the biggest of these nunataks being Hvannadalshnjúkur (see picture on page 55).

As mentioned before, the physician and naturalist Sveinn Pálsson was the first to climb Öræfajökull. His ascent is reported in his treatise on glaciology. He set off from the farm Kvísker on the August 11, 1794 and climbed a peak in the south-east part of the glacier together with an assistant. According to his measurements of the altitude and his description of the ascent the peak in question is considered to have been Knappur (1927 m). The stretch from there across the caldera to Hvannadalshnjúkur is about four km. The first to climb the latter peak were the Norwegian Hans Frisak in 1813 and the Englishman Fr.W.W. Howell in 1891.

The best direct route to Hvannadalshnjúkur, apart from the snowmobile route described above, is from the farm Sandfell in Öræfi. From the ice cap Snæbreið snowmobiles can be driven right down to the foot of Hvannadalshnjúkur, where there is an excellent place for camping (see picture right, on page 75).

The picture above shows Hvannadalshnjúkur, bathed in the morning sun, as it looks from Snæbreið (2041 m), which is still throwing a shadow right to its foot. - Below the crew of the snowmobile Gosi are having dinner at a camp on the top of Snæbreið on a calm and sunny day. Even the photographer can be spotted in the snowmobile mirror with Hvannadalshnjúkur in the background.

Below to the right a snowmobile is leaving Hermannaskarð for a climb on to Öræfajökull. In the background is Breiðamerkurjökull and Þuríðartindur is to the right.

74

Hvannadalshnjúkur takes on varying forms, depending on the degree of daylight. A majestic sight is the background of this camp at the foot of the highest peak in Iceland which now has donned its finest garb in the midday sun. The easiest route from the camp to the top is across the ridge to the right, past the rock-face, and then askew up the mountain side where it disappears behind the summit. The route is very steep and the snow is usually very hard. The summit is a rather small snow cap, often very icy. It goes without saying that when the visibility is good the view in every direction from Hvannadalshnjúkur is quite breathtaking.

From its base the height of the peak of Hvannadalshnjúkur itself is less than 250 m. It is very steep, however, calling for great care due to the numerous crevasses and glassy ice. Hvannadalshnjúkur can vary a great deal in appearance as the light changes. But somehow the feeling of supreme grandeur is most pronounced when the last rays of the setting sun colour its ice-covered peak in gold while the surrounding ice surface below is submerged in dark blue shadows, as in the picture on the right.

In clear weather there is, of course, a breath-taking view in all directions, but often the lowland below the 1000 m altitude level is overclouded, even if the glacier to the north is completely clear. The border mountains Hrútafjallstindar and Skaftafellsfjöll with the Þumall (The Thumb), a pinnacle of basalt, tower against the ice cap, whereas the nunataks Þórðarhyrna and Grímsfjall can be seen farther away.

Above is a view from Hvannadalshnjúkur to the north-west over Vatnajökull. Hrútfjallstindar are the nearest, but farther away, near the edge of the glacier, are the Skaftafell mountains, where the rock Þumall and Miðfellstindur peak may be seen. Over Skaftafellsjökull and Morsárdalur there is a cloud cover, penetrated only by the highest peaks. On the other hand, the sky is clear over Vatnajökull where Þórðarhyrna, Hábunga and Grímsfjall can be seen.

The picture on the right (p. 77) shows the rays of the setting sun gild Hvannadalshnjúkur, which towers majestically above the dark-blue ice-cap. Some travellers can be seen standing on the summit, but in the blue haze further below part of the Öræfajökull caldera can be faintly discerned.

When the wide expanses of the Vatnajökull firn are draped by the first morning sun in its profusion of glittering rays, a myriad of ice crystals glisten all over the glacier (see picture above). There is no parallel, except perhaps an aerial view of a large city at night when thousands of lights twinkle in unending splendour. This phenomenon is unknown when the sun is low in the evening. Nor does it appear in the morning if the air is warm. - The picture on the right (p.81) is a view from Snæbreið over Breiðamerkurjökull.

80

The first eruption of Öræfajökull after the settlement of Iceland was in 1362. It was one of the biggest explosive eruptions known to have occurred anywhere in the world in historical times. In this eruption a whole settlement of 30-40 farms was completely destroyed, and temporarily all the inhabited area in the vicinity of Öræfajökull is believed to have been abandoned.

In his treatise Sveinn Pálsson quotes the following report on the destruction that occurred in 1362: 'One morning about milking-time at the farm of Svínafell a shepherd named Hallur and some milkmaids heard a thundering crash from the glacier just above the farm. They all got panic-stricken, but shortly afterwards there was another crash, even more powerful. Then the shepherd is reported to have said that it would not be wise to wait for the third one and without a further ado he took to his heels to the mountain above, reaching a cave, still called Flosahellir, not far away from the farm. Then came the third crash, and at the same moment the glacier exploded with an enormous bang. Water and ice filled every ravine in the mountain and washed away all the people and the livestock in the settlement below or buried them all in deep mud, sand and glacial debris inside the farmhouses, with the exception of the shepherd.'

During this eruption very large amounts of rhyolite-tephra burst out of the volcano. It has been estimated that it could have covered the whole country with a 10 cm thick layer, but fortunately most of this tephra fell in the sea.

The second eruption of Öræfajökull started on August 4, 1727 with two strong earthquakes. Then two outlet glaciers advanced, suddenly, covering the lowlands with mud and ice.

We are told that tephra and volcanic bombs fell continuously for three days, darkening the sky. The eruption continued until May 24, 1728. This second eruption was, however, not as violent as the first, and since then there have been no signs of the fire beneath the ice cover of Öræfajökull.

Breiðamerkurjökull is one of the Icelandic outlet glaciers which dip their snouts into a glacier lake where icebergs break off for a free ride on the water. The black stripes on the glacier, lateral and medial moraines, emerge when the advancing ice of an outlet glacier is split by an opposing nunatak and reunited below it. The moraines consist of stones and clay eroded by the outlet glacier from the mountain sides and transported down to the lowlands. On Breiðamerkurjökull these moraines are derived from Esjufjöll and Máfabyggðir, showing clearly the direction of the ice movement.

The ice floes on the Breiðamerkur glacier lake (right) are not all big, but they vary a great deal in shape and colour. On their travel across the lake they often hit the bottom, melt and break up until they are small enough to be brought down to the sea by the river Jökulsá á Breiðamerkursandi.

glacier lakes

There are two types of lakes that are created or maintained by glaciers, apart from ones caused by the effects of volcanic heat as in the case of Grímsvötn (see page 58). Glacier lakes are often formed at the snout of outlet glaciers when they retreat as a result of ameliorating climate. Over a long period of time an outlet glacier builds up an end moraine, but it also buries its snout considerably deeper into the ground above the moraine. When it has withdrawn further a glacier lake is left in the depression, and the melt-water that has accumulated in the lake will find its way through the lowest part of the moraine to the sea, forming a glacial river.

All this is illustrated in the picture on page 85, showing the snout of the outlet glacier Fjalljökull, a part of Öræfajökull, reaching into the glacier lake Fjallsárlón. The foot of the Breiðamerkurjökull once reached much further towards the coast than it does now. There was no glacier lake there then, but the Jökulsá á Breiðamerkursandi, the shortest big river in Iceland, came straight out from under the foot of the glacier, crossing the narrow sand beach and flowing direct into the Atlantic Ocean. Now there is a big and deep glacier lake at the end of the outlet glacier with enormous icebergs breaking off the snout and floating on the glacier lake as shown in the pictures on pages 82, 83 and 84. When Þorvaldur Thoroddsen, the naturalist, crossed Breiðamerkursandur in 1894, the distance from the glacier´s edge to the sea-shore was only 256 m so that heavy seas brought driftwood right up to the glacier. Breiðamerkurjökull is the only Icelandic glacier which has been so close to the sea. The glacial river Jökulsá á Breiðamerkursandi was then deemed to be the most difficult one to cross south of Vatnajökull, so it was frequently by-passed by crossing the glacier snout. Now motor vehicles can cross this river by a suspension bridge just below the glacier lake. In the picture of Breiðamerkurjökull on page 82 several medial moraines are visible. These are ridges of rock debris that are eroded from each side of nunataks as the glacier slides forward. Right below the nunataks these ridges are reunited in one medial moraine.

A view of the Breiðamerkursandur glacier lake. Ærfjall is to the left and Breiðamerkurfjall to the right, but between them is Fjallsjökull, an outlet glacier extending from Öræfajökull. The farm Fjall was situated near the foot of Breiðamerkurjökull from about 900 A.D. until it was buried under the glacier in the years between 1695 and 1709. Now its site has re-emerged as the glacier retired. - Many of the ice floes in the Breiðamerkursandur lake are of peculiar shapes.

This aerial view (right) of the snout of Fjallsjökull to the east of Öræfajökull reveals many rows of old moraines. The Fjallsá lake collects the meltwater, which then proceeds to the sea. The works of man look tiny in comparison with those of nature. Just below the lake there is a fairly big bridge, barely visible, the picture being taken from a considerable height.

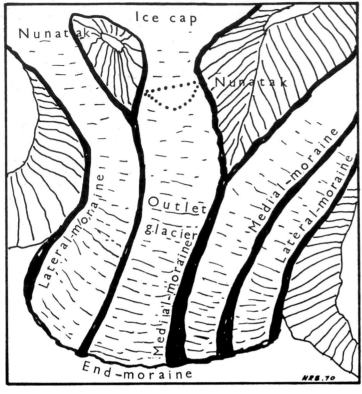

At Breiðamerkurjökull these medial moraines come from Esjufjöll and Máfabyggðir (see map on page 52). The drawing on the left shows how medial moraines and lateral moraines are formed, the latter occurring along the sides of an outlet glacier.

On the drawing the dots on the outlet glacier between the nunataks indicate the moving speed at different points across its ice stream. Marks put in a straight line across it will after a reasonable time be found at the places indicated, showing the relative speed of different parts of a cross section of the stream. The greatest speed is in the middle, whereas it is much slower on both sides.

The medial moraines also show very clearly the direction of movement in the outlet glaciers, as can be seen on the aerial views of Skeiðarárjökull illustrated here (on the left at bottom and on the right). In the top left-hand corner of both these pictures is the lake Grænalón, a good specimen of the second type of glacier lakes. Grænalón is an ice-dammed lake. It was formed in a valley by the side of the glacier-filled Skeiðarárdalur valley. The water in this lake consists only of melt-water from the glacier as there is no volcanic heat here.

The water level in Grænalón rises until the water can either overflow the glacier dam or, what happens quite frequently when the water level exceeds nine tenths of the thickness of the edge of the outlet glacier damming up the lake, the water lifts the glacier edge and the lake is emptied by means of a sudden glacier burst below the glacier down into the river Súla. For a long time these glacier bursts remained a mystery.

The lateral and medial moraines of Skeiðarárjökull clearly show the direction of its movement. In the top left-hand corner of the picture the outlet glacier closes a side-valley where Grænalón ('Green Lake') is formed between Grænafjall close to the glacier and Mt. Eggjar.

The nature of Grænalón remained a mystery for a long time. It is an ice-dammed lake which intermittently gives rise to glacier floods in the river Súla. At one time Grænalón was identified with Grímsvötn because volcanic or geothermal heat was thought to be the cause of these glacier floods, and it was even thought that the glacier floods in the river Skeiðará originated in it before the connection between Skeiðarárdalur and Grímsvötn became evident. The surface level of Grænalón used to be at a height of 620 m, being drained by the River Núpsá when the level of the lake was at a maximum. Since then Skeiðarárjökull has shrunk in the area where it dams up the lake. Therefore, the water level of the lake has subsided so that none of the water finds its way to the Núpsá. On the other hand, the lake is emptied under the edge of the glacier at intervals of a few years, or is drained to some extent by a brook that flows along the edge of the glacier near Eggjar and Eystrafjall, which is to the left in this picture below Grænalón. The Vatnajökull ice-cap is in the back-ground.

87

winter snow

The winter snow comes to all of us who live in northerly countries without our having to look for it in the mountains or on glaciers. Those who are fond of skiing welcome the winter snow and young people accustomed to winter sports from their childhood will always remember the delight and freedom of the wide expanses where everything is clean and white and any direction offers a possible route. Then there is the silence of the wilderness.

Explorers of the Polar wastes have described the immense snowfields there as 'the great white silence', but even in the skiing areas of inhabited countries it is possible for members of a small party of skiers to experience this silence of the wide expanses. A young man´s skiing experience on a clear and frosty mid-winter night will long be remembered - the whole sky being completely covered with the amber–green flashing folds of the northern lights, and the soft and gentle carpet of snow reflecting the green hue of the sky, mingling with the blue shadows in the snow.

Even the most romantic description of such a night will never do justice to the fascination burned into one´s mind for a whole lifetime, although in actual fact it can undeniably be a costly nuisance both for individuals and the community at large. The snow can disrupt communications and impede work in general, prevent the use of pasture in winter and cause damage to property.

Anyhow, the winter snow is an annual visitor on every farm and in every town in northerly countries. Therefore, we might as well be prepared for its arrival and fully enjoy its beauty and charm. In Iceland and other Nordic countries skis were first used as a means of transportation between farms and villages when the winter snow covered all the land. This use of skis is no less important today for nature lovers, although motor-driven means of transport on land and in the air have firmly established themselves for all practical purposes. Cross-country skiing with camping equipment for travel in the mountains in late winter or early spring can be refreshing and exhilarating, and in many ways the mountains look quite different from their summer garb when they are covered with winter snow. It is often like looking at a different landscape altogether.

That is how it is with Botnssúlur, the peaks at the far end of Hvalfjörður to the north of Þingvellir. Skis are of little use for climbing here, however, due to the steepness of the mountain slopes. The highest peak is 1095 m, and the others are not much lower. Botnssúlur are free from snow in summer, except that some snow patches on the northern slopes may not melt every year. In winter the snow covers these peaks with an attractive mantle which is never exactly the same because the snow is as changeable as winter fashions. The layers of snow vary with the wind, and icing on the rocks depends on the interaction of frost, sunshine and wind.

Botnssúlur is the name of a few mountain peaks at the far end of Hvalfjörður. They are in a northerly direction from Þingvellir. The highest peak is 1095 m, but they are all more or less of the same height. These pictures were taken while the winter snow cover still remained on April 9. In summer Botnssúlur are free of snow, except for a few snow patches that often linger in hollows on the slopes.

The winter snow can vary in form in very much the same way as glacial ice. Above there are peculiar stripes, caused by the wind, in a ravine in Mt. Eggjar near Grænalón.

Even lowland lava near inhabited areas may acquire a snow cover of extraordinary beauty when the low winter sun sets off clearly every irregularity by the interplay of light and shadows (see picture on the right).

92

icing

Icing may be of many different kinds due to differences in external conditions. Icicles are formed where dripping water freezes. They are common both in nature and on house-eaves. Hoarfrost in the form of feathers and fans on window glass is also well known. Icing can, of course, be formed on any exposed object. Rime on trees is of outstanding beauty, especially in the first rays of the morning sun. When frost arrives suddenly in autumn, very beautiful rime formations can often be observed on the moss of lava fields, particularly near openings in the lava. Thick lava streams are often very porous, containing considerable amounts of warm and humid air in the autumn. When the temperature falls below freezing point, this air flows out through the openings where condensation of its humidity takes place with the result that the surrounding moss looks as if it were covered with exotic white flowers. They are, however, very fine leaves of hoarfrost, consisting of a number of ice needles which glitter when they are caught by the winter sun.

Near hot springs where warm vapour drizzles over the immediate vicinity, there are very interesting icing formations on plants when the vapour freezes.

The cave Raufarhólshellir is remarkable at any time of the year, but in early spring and in winter when the snow does not prevent its accessibility, spectacular ice formations attract great interest. Besides the icicles hanging down from the ceiling, ice pillars (stalagmites) rise from the floor where the water dripping from the icicles has frozen. The whole floor near the entrance of the cave is covered with slippery ice, so crampons are advisable, but this fairy-tale world is certainly worth a visit. Farther inside the cave there is total darkness so that good lighting is essential.

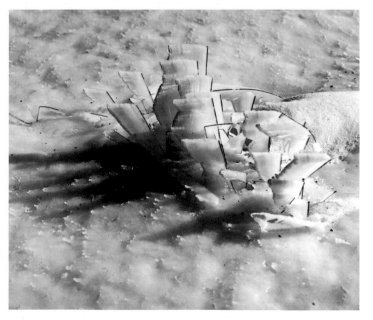

In many places icing is the result of warm or humid air coming in contact with solid objects in frosty weather. Above there are fine hoarfrost formations that look like flower petals. This hoarfrost was formed on lava moss. The picture to the left shows ice-covered straws near a geyser. Steam and hot water is emitted by the hot spring and the moisture freezes on straws, which the wind turns into ice plates. - The picture to the right was taken in the Raufarhólshellir ('Raufarhóll Cave') in winter. Icicles hang from the ceiling, stretching towards their counterparts, the stalagmites, which rise from the floor where the water-drops from the icicles freeze as well.

hot springs under ice

In many places in Iceland hot springs can be found under ice, where they sometimes create huge ice caves by melting the covering snow. Among well known places of this kind is the north-west slopes of Mt. Hrafntinnusker near Landmannalaugar, east of Hekla. Hrafntinnusker is 1080 m high. It does not have a permanent ice cap, only snow or ice patches on its slopes. If there are hot springs under the firn, crevasses develop in the ice cover with ice caves underneath. Even if there are hot springs on the floors of the caves, they are quite accessible, but inside there is a high degree of humidity, both due to the steam from the hot springs and water dripping from the ceiling above. From

the outside it is easy to see how the firn has been gently sinking due to the heat underneath as the yearly ice layers in the firn have bent above the openings into the caves. This shows the plasticity of glacier ice. It can easily bend if its movement is slow enough. On the other hand, it is brittle and will easily break if it is subjected to sudden and powerful stresses, resulting in the formation of crevasses. Sometimes, there-fore, part of the ceiling of an ice cave tumbles down so that great care is advisable on the part of any would-be explorers. Due to the melting of the ceiling a most peculiar bowl-like surface is formed with ice tops and ridges in between. These formations can be seen in the picture above although it is somewhat marred by steam and vapour which make photography rather difficult.

On the slopes of Hrafntinnusker near Landmannalaugar there is glacial firn even though there is no ice cap on the mountain peak. But on these slopes there are also hot springs which melt deep ice caves in the firn. The picture on the right clearly shows the plastic nature of glacial ice which can shrink and bend if the movement is slow enough, whereas it will crack or break if it is subjected to sudden stresses.

100

On a spring night there is a beautiful view from Vatnajökull (above) to the north over the west part of Kverkfjöll and the Hveradalur. The steam springs melt away the ice at the top end of Hveradalur, forming huge ice-cauldrons in the glacier where the ice has been softened by the subterranean heat. In the background to the left are the Dyngjufjöll mountains with the volcano Askja, which erupted last time in 1961. The peculiar table mountain Herðubreið on the Mývatnsöræfi is in the background to the right. The sides of table mountains are steep and there is a precipitous rock wall around the top, which in turn is either flat or slightly conical.

To the north of the lake in the southern part of the Hveradalur in the Kverkfjöll area there is a number of boiling mud pots (solfataras) in very colourful surroundings (right). To the north of this area the valley is rather shallow, rising gradually to a thin cross-ridge which practically divides the valley in two dissimilar parts, but to the north of this ridge the valley is much deeper with very steep mountain slopes, particularly on the west side (see picture on p. 110).

108

rhyolite

Rhyolite is a fine-textured volcanic rock, composed mostly of quarts (silicon dioxide) and feldspar. It is of many different colours: It can be yellow, pink, reddish, grey-blue and green. There is even a black glassy variety, hrafntinna (obsidian), formed by the rapid cooling of rhyolite magma, mainly on the surface of rhyolite lava-fields, which, however, are very uncommon in Iceland. It is no wonder, therefore, that this multicolored rock attracts the attention of travellers, even from a considerable distance. When mountain tops consist of rhyolite, they often look as if they were bathed in sunshine even if the sky is overcast.

The difference between the mineral composition of basaltic lava and rhyolite is that the silicon content of rhyolite is higher than in basalt. In point of fact, the same Icelandic volcanoes sometimes produce basalt, sometimes intermediate material, and sometimes rhyolite. It has been shown by recent research that the silicium proportion of the magma issuing from some volcanoes increases proportionately to the length of the time that passes between eruptions. When the time between two eruptions is short, the eruption material mainly consists of basaltic lava, but when several centuries elapse between eruptions, explosive eruptions are more likely, producing mainly rhyolite tephra. For example, the volcano Askja erupted rhyolite in 1875, but basalt in 1961, and Snæfellsjökull (see p. 46-49) has erupted rhyolite at least twice. The reason is believed to be that there are separate pockets of magma at a depth of only a few km, although this magma owes its origin to a common source. At the top of such magma pockets lighter materials like silica concentrate when a long time elapses between eruptions, and the next eruption will be an acid-explosive one due to gases released through cooling.

The Torfajökull area is rich in rhyolite formations. The top picture was taken to the south-west of Landmannalaugar, but the lower picture was taken in the slightly acid Námshraun lava with a view across the river Námskvísl to Suðurnámur.

On the left is the west side of the northern part of the Hveradalur valley in the Kverkfjöll area, all dotted with steamy hot springs. Jagged rocks decorate the edge of the slope, which, however, provides the shortest route to the place where the best view is to be had over this spectacularly colourful area. The Vatnajökull ice cap is in the background.

fumaroles

It was mentioned before that in the volcanic parts of Iceland there are 15 high temperature or steam areas. The high temperature areas also contain hot springs, often including the spouting type and steam vents, especially on high ground, which sometimes develop into mud pots, also called fumaroles or solfataras. It is interesting to note that the temperature in the hot springs is apparently highest where rhyolite is the main rock and therefore these areas seem to have some connection with rhyolite eruptions. If a steam spring area has a very high temperatr1re, it can almost invariably be linked with a recent volcanic activity.

In the night before the May 17, 1724 the 'Mývatn Fires' started with a great explosion on the slopes of Mt. Krafla, north-east of Lake Mývatn, and a new crater, called Víti ('Hell'), was formed. After the volcanic eruption finished, the crater was an impressive fumarole, i.e. a boiling mud pot, for more than a whole century. Then it slowly lost its power, and today it is only a big water-filled basin, now called Stóra Víti ('Big Hell'). Now there is another big fumarole, called Litla Víti ('Little Hell') at the bottom of a ravine near by. This mud pot has built up a cone around the hole where the blue mud is boiling. The whole area around this ravine is very colorful and several openings of older hot springs and dried-out mud pots show how the hot spring activity moves around as old mud pots disappear and new ones come into being. A similar area with boiling mud pots and steam jets spouting high up into the air is situated east of Námafjall, due east of Mývatn. There, too, the blue mud boils in pits of different sizes. In some the liquid is thin, but in others it is in the form of a thick paste (see page 114).

Above is the colourful side of the Krafla ravine, just below the mud pot Litla Víti. The picture below is of a dried-out clay area with small mud pot holes still boiling underneath.

This large mud pot (right) in the lower part of the Krafla ravine is called Litla Víti ('Little Hell'). The blue clay boils and bubbles in a cone-shaped crater, built up by the mud splashes.

112

In the steam spring area to the east of Námafjall in the Mývatn District (picture on the left), there is a large number of mud pots (solfataras) where the blue mud boils and simmers, sending up air bubbles in the thick mud which, when bursting, form concentric circles on the surface of the mud pot.

A complete contrast to the mud pots is this clear-blue hot spring near Geysir in Haukadalur (above). The water is so clear that its surface is barely discernible. Down in the spring the walls are covered with sinter.

hot springs

Most famous of the Icelandic spouting hot springs is Geysir in Haukadalur, which has given its name to all similar hot springs in the world. Geysir spouts very seldom now, but nearby there are several boiling hot water springs, some of which erupt regularily. The bowl of Geysir is 18 m in diameter and about 1.3 m deep. The pipe reaching down from the bowl is about 20 m deep and 3 m wide at the top, but narrows as it goes down.

The name of Geysir in Haukadalur has in fact provided the general term for a spouting hot spring, known in English as 'geyser'. Eruptions of Geysir, as shown in the photograph on the left, have for a long time drawn visitors to the place. In a mighty eruption the water and steam column may reach a height of 60-70 m. Today, however an eruption of Geysir is a rare occurrence unless it is activated by soap. Another but smaller 'geyser' in the same fissure, Strokkur ('Churn') erupts regularly, however.

A spectacular hot spring area is located at Hveravellir on Kjölur near the Langjökull glacier. Most of the hot springs there are rather small. Some are calm and clear-blue ponds, while others eject boiling water and steam. Many of the hot springs have created real works of art out of the sinter that accumulates around their openings, as shown in the pictures on this page.

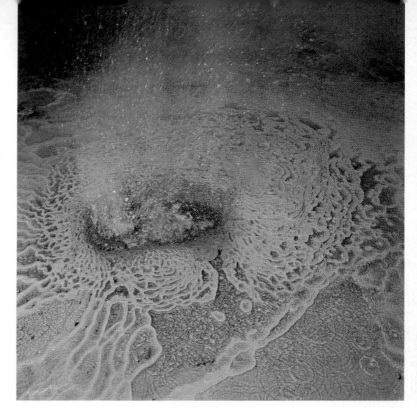

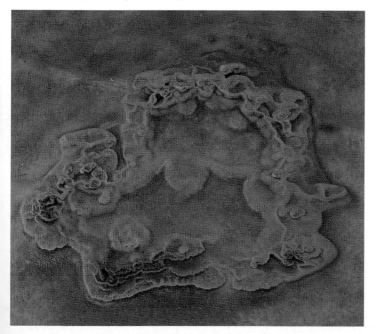

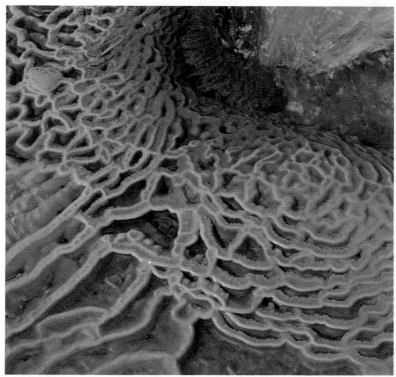

The bowl of Geysir is situated in the top of a low mound, built up of layers of siliceous sinter from the spring water. It is believed that Geysir and Strokkur were both formed in a great earthquake in 1294. We are told in the Odda-verja Annal that '...at Haukadalur two big hot water springs came into existence, whereas others which had been there before disappeared'. Research on the time needed to build up a siliceous sinter mound of this size and dated volcanic ash layers in the soil below it support this dating.

After 1800 Geysir is often mentioned in foreign books on travel in Iceland, but around 1900 Geysir eruptions decreased in number, and in 1916 they stopped completely. In 1935 the eruptions started again after the water level in the bowl had been lowered, reducing the cooling of the water surface in the bowl.

The Geysir eruptions were then, and later, studied by Dr. Trausti Einarsson, who explains them as follows: 'Into the vertical channel of Geysir the water enters at a temperature of 125° C through smaller passages coming from greater depths. At the bottom of the main tube the boiling point is about 132 °C when the water is standing high in the bowl, and therefore the water does not boil at the bottom. At a depth of 10 m in the pipe the boiling point is about 120° C, and there the temperature sometimes reaches that level and even higher. Boiling of the water at that point generates an eruption. It is not sufficient, however, for the water to reach a boiling point to start an eruption. The water has to be overheated by 4-5° C above the boiling point. The boiling then generates a sudden explosion, and the water above is thrown up into the air. The explosive boiling produces the well-known rumbling noise just before the starting of an eruption, which is really the result of a long chain of explosions in the water. In powerful Geysir eruptions the water column may reach a height of 60-70 m, and it may continue for about 10 minutes. Towards the end a steam column emerges from the nearly empty tube. Strokkur is of a similar type and is situated on the same fissure as Geysir, but it is much smaller.

The deepest hole drilled so far in Iceland is about 3000 m, and the highest temperature recorded at the bottom of a drilled hole is above 380°C.

At Hveravellir (top and bottom left) layers of sinter have piled up to form large domes around the hot springs. Near the top of the main dome there is a calm and clear-blue hot spring in a good-sized bowl, while further up there is one called 'Roaring Mound' or 'Roaring Geyser', a cinter cone with two openings.

The photograph on the right is a view into one of the openings of 'Roaring Geyser' at Hveravellir. In former days, when it got this name, it was not considered particularly silent as it then emitted big jets of steam.

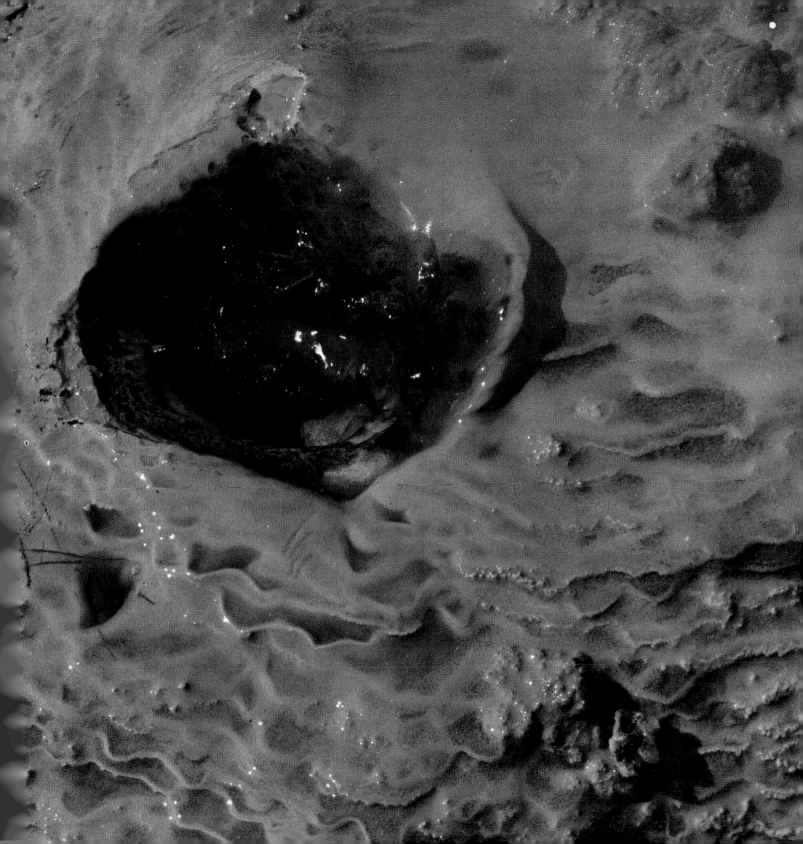

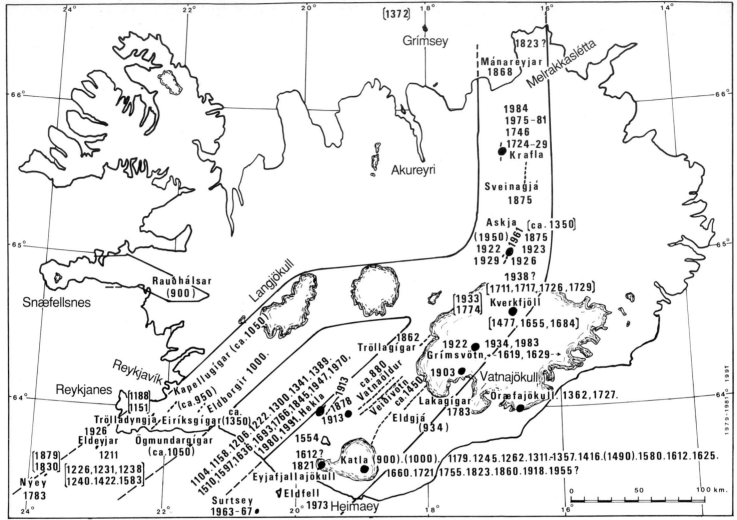

On the map above areas of volcanic activity in Iceland after the Ice Age are marked. The westernmost area is the Snæfellsnes Peninsula. A much bigger area is the belt from the Reykjanes Peninsula to Langjökull Glacier, a direct continuation of the Reykjanes Ridge, which in turn is a part of the Mid-Atlantic Ridge. By far the biggest and most active volcanic zone in Iceland is the belt from Surtsey, the new volcanic island to the south of Iceland, through the Vestmannaeyjar (Heimaey), the north-western part of Vatnajökull Glacier (Grímsvötn), to the Melrakkaslétta Peninsula in the North. This zone is about 70 km wide in its southern part, but it is somewhat narrower north of Vatnajökull. It has been suggested that the intense volcanic activity of this zone might indicate that the Mid-Atlantic Ridge is moving eastwards in this area. The fourth volcanic zone in Iceland is highlighted by the Öræfajökull Glacier on the southern edge of Vatnajökull, slightly east of the main volcanic zone.

This map also shows volcanic activity in Iceland during historical time, i.e. volcanic eruptions after 874 A.D. Years in brackets indicate

that exact dating is uncertain. Where the year is preceded by 'ca', the date of the eruption is very uncertain but most likely within the century of the year indicated. Years in square brackets indicate that the exact place of the eruption is unknown. Where the date is followed by a question mark, it is not certain that there was an eruption at the place concerned that year. In the northern part of the eastern volcanic zone in Iceland is the Krafla caldera and the associated 80-km long fissure swarm. Here a rifting episode started in 1975. (See pp 215-228: Krafla eruption 1975-84). The horizontal extension observed during the last Krafla eruption confirms a drift of the two parts of Iceland on either side of the volcanic zone by 1 cm/year in each direction. A point of reference is an episode of similar volcanic activity in the same area about 230 years earlier, i.e. in 1724-1746.

The rifting occurs periodically in short active pulses, and between them a continuous inflation of the caldera is caused by a $5 m^3$/sec inflow of magma into a magma chamber at a depth of 3 km.

volcanoes

There is often a considerable relationship between volcanic and hot spring activity. Sometimes new hot springs are forerunners of volcanic eruptions, and often hot spring areas develop on the spot after the cessation of the volcanic activity.

It is a volcanic eruption when hot materials break through the earth crust or when gases explode underneath the surface, resulting in the formation of an explosive crater, even if no lava or tephra comes to the surface. Spouting hot springs are not classified as volcanic eruptions in spite of the relationship between the two. In and under the earth´s crust is magma, at least in volcanic areas. The term magma applies to the molten rock still within the earth. That it is molten is naturally a guess because no one has ever seen magma proper, only the volcanic material that comes to the surface of the earth during eruptions, but such a material may have changed due to its contact with the upper rock-layers of the crust and reduced pressure.

Geologically Iceland is a young country, almost completely built up by volcanic rocks. The basalt formation, which forms the oldest part of the country, was built up in Tertiary times of lava layers one on top of the other to a pile of some kilometres. During the subsequent ice ages the eruptions continued under the ice sheet and then the tuff mountains were built up. In discussions of volcanoes in Iceland, this term usually applies only to volcanic areas where eruptions have taken place since the last ice-age, which is considered to have ended about 10.000 years ago. These post-glacial volcanic areas are mainly in a broad belt lying over the middle of the country from south-west to north-east, split into two parts at the southern end as shown on the maps on pp. 120 and 161. Outside this belt, however, are the areas of Snæfellsnes and Öræfajökull. The direction of the volcanic fissures in the southern part of this area is mainly from south-west to north-east, but north of Vatnajökull the prevailing direction of the fissures is S to N.

It is reasonable to ask how many volcanoes there are in Iceland and how many of them are active. This question, however, is not an easy one to answer. In this connection it should be kept in mind that not all volcanoes are mountains. A volcano may be a fissure or a depression. Many explosive craters are examples of the latter. Several volcanic cones or a row of craters may develop along one fissure. If they all erupted at the same time, it is reasonable to call them all just one volcano. But if a new fissure opens up a century or so later, either as a continuation of the former or parallel to whether the new fissure is a separate volcano or not.

Hekla is Iceland´s most famous volcano. Above is a view from the summit of Hekla over the top crater, which erupted in 1947, towards the lava of 1913, Laufafell and Rauðfossafjöll.

Below is a side view of Hekla as seen from Þjórsárdalur, after the 1947 Hekla eruption..

The Lakagígar craters number 100-115, all of them in a row in a fissure lying in a SW-NE direction, which came into being in 1783. The whole fissure is about 25 km long. The tuff mountain Laki, which is situated near the centre of the fissure, burst open on both sides far up into the slopes during the eruption. Above is a view from Laki along the crater row to the south-west, but below is a view from a 90 m high red cinder cone situated 3.5 km to the south-west along the crater row to Laki.

Another difficulty arises when a new lava flow completely inundates old craters. Furthermore, volcanoes under glaciers are common in Iceland and they are very difficult to count. Based on the period since the last ice age, the number of volcanoes in Iceland has been estimated to be definitely above 150 and most likely more than 200. But how many of these volcanoes are active, i.e. how many of them have erupted in historical time, which in Iceland covers the last 11 centuries, indicating that they might erupt again? The number of active volcanoes in Iceland has on this basis been estimated to be about 30. The total number of eruptions in Iceland since the settlement is nearly 200 because during the last few centuries there has been a volcanic eruption every 5th or 6th year on the average. Thus, Iceland is one of the most active volcanic areas on earth, but it is not least the variety of the Icelandic volcanoes which makes them interesting to volcanologists for field study. Almost all existing types of volcanoes can be found here and some of them are very rare outside Iceland.

Volcanoes formed by the opening of a fissure usually erupt only once. The most famous volcano in Iceland, Mt. Hekla, does not, however, follow this rule as this firy mountain ridge has been built up in several eruptions out of a fissure that has the usual SW-NE direction prevailing in this area. When the eruption started on March 29 1947, the Hekla cracked open along the whole mountain ridge, which has this direction, with the lava flowing down the slopes on either side.

Ljótipollur ('Ugly pool'), near Landmannalaugar, is one of the most beautiful explosive craters in Iceland. In form it is reminiscent of both calderas and explosive fissures. In explosive eruptions the volcanic material consists almost exclusively of cinders (tephra), and there is very little or no lava.

hot springs

Most famous of the Icelandic spouting hot springs is Geysir in Haukadalur, which has given its name to all similar hot springs in the world. Geysir spouts very seldom now, but nearby there are several boiling hot water springs, some of which erupt regularily. The bowl of Geysir is 18 m in diameter and about 1.3 m deep. The pipe reaching down from the bowl is about 20 m deep and 3 m wide at the top, but narrows as it goes down.

The name of Geysir in Haukadalur has in fact provided the general term for a spouting hot spring, known in English as 'geyser'. Eruptions of Geysir, as shown in the photograph on the left, have for a long time drawn visitors to the place. In a mighty eruption the water and steam column may reach a height of 60-70 m. Today, however an eruption of Geysir is a rare occurrence unless it is activated by soap. Another but smaller 'geyser' in the same fissure, Strokkur ('Churn') erupts regularly, however.

A spectacular hot spring area is located at Hveravellir on Kjölur near the Langjökull glacier. Most of the hot springs there are rather small. Some are calm and clear-blue ponds, while others eject boiling water and steam. Many of the hot springs have created real works of art out of the sinter that accumulates around their openings, as shown in the pictures on this page.

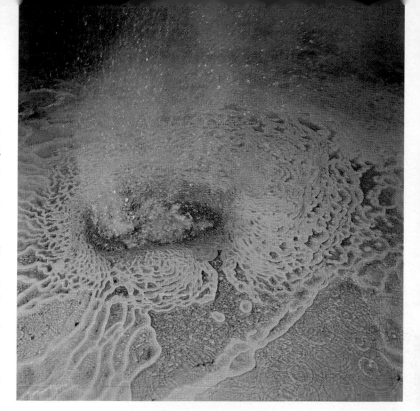

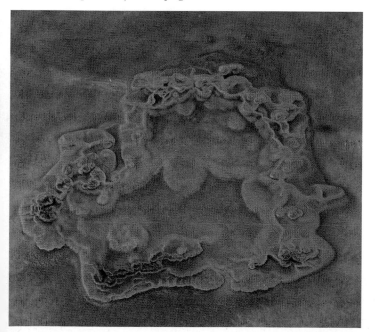

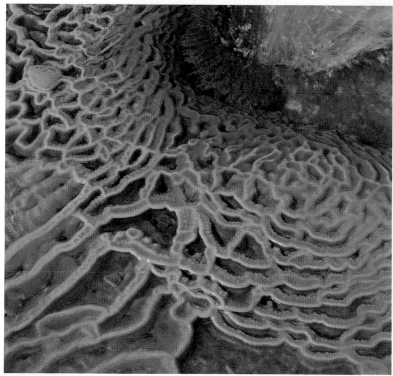

The bowl of Geysir is situated in the top of a low mound, built up of layers of siliceous sinter from the spring water. It is believed that Geysir and Strokkur were both formed in a great earthquake in 1294. We are told in the Odda-verja Annal that '...at Haukadalur two big hot water springs came into existence, whereas others which had been there before disappeared'. Research on the time needed to build up a siliceous sinter mound of this size and dated volcanic ash layers in the soil below it support this dating.

After 1800 Geysir is often mentioned in foreign books on travel in Iceland, but around 1900 Geysir eruptions decreased in number, and in 1916 they stopped completely. In 1935 the eruptions started again after the water level in the bowl had been lowered, reducing the cooling of the water surface in the bowl.

The Geysir eruptions were then, and later, studied by Dr. Trausti Einarsson, who explains them as follows: 'Into the vertical channel of Geysir the water enters at a temperature of 125° C through smaller passages coming from greater depths. At the bottom of the main tube the boiling point is about 132 °C when the water is standing high in the bowl, and therefore the water does not boil at the bottom. At a depth of 10 m in the pipe the boiling point is about 120° C, and there the temperature sometimes reaches that level and even higher. Boiling of the water at that point generates an eruption. It is not sufficient, however, for the water to reach a boiling point to start an eruption. The water has to be overheated by 4-5° C above the boiling point. The boiling then generates a sudden explosion, and the water above is thrown up into the air. The explosive boiling produces the well-known rumbling noise just before the starting of an eruption, which is really the result of a long chain of explosions in the water. In powerful Geysir eruptions the water column may reach a height of 60-70 m, and it may continue for about 10 minutes. Towards the end a steam column emerges from the nearly empty tube. Strokkur is of a similar type and is situated on the same fissure as Geysir, but it is much smaller.

The deepest hole drilled so far in Iceland is about 3000 m, and the highest temperature recorded at the bottom of a drilled hole is above 380°C.

At Hveravellir (top and bottom left) layers of sinter have piled up to form large domes around the hot springs. Near the top of the main dome there is a calm and clear-blue hot spring in a good-sized bowl, while further up there is one called 'Roaring Mound' or 'Roaring Geyser', a cinter cone with two openings.

The photograph on the right is a view into one of the openings of 'Roaring Geyser' at Hveravellir. In former days, when it got this name, it was not considered particularly silent as it then emitted big jets of steam.

Mt. Hekla does not only present a spectacular sight from the lowland to the south, but also from the highlands and from the sea. Viewed in the direction of the fissure, its main contours are like those of a cone (stratovolcano), but a side-view from the Þjórsárdalur valley makes it look like a typical volcanic ridge.

The length of the Hekla is about 10 km, and the fissure which opens up when the mountain itself erupts is about 5 km long. After the 1947 eruption the highest peak of Hekla was 1491 m (see picture on p. 121).

Mt. Hekla´s eruption material is mixed, i.e. there is both tephra and lava. Its history of eruptions over a period of about 7000 years can be traced with fair reliability. The mountain itself has been built up almost entirely in post-glacial time, but it rests on a foundation of mainly palagonite tuffs and breccias (Móberg) from the ice-age.

The Hekla was a mountain at the time of the settlement as its oldest name indicates (Heklufell, 'Mount Hekla'). The Hekla erupted several times before the settlement as many eruptions must have been needed to built up such a sizable mountain. This is also indicated by numerous prehistoric tephra layers. But a long time must have elapsed since the last eruption as the lava fields were covered with vegetation at the time of the settlement. Otherwise the settlers would not have built their farms in lava areas near Hekla.

The first written sources about an eruption in Hekla are to be found in the annals of 1104, which has the following entry: 'The first eruption of fire in Heklufell'. This means no doubt that this was the first eruption of the Hekla after the settlement, and now it is considered quite certain that the Þjórsárdalur valley was devastated and abandoned as early as the time of this eruption. It is likely that no less than 2-3 centuries had passed then since the last eruption of the Hekla, except possibly for small eruptions which had not attracted much attention, if they happened after the settlement at all. Never since has such a long time elapsed between Hekla eruptions. The next eruptions occurred in 1158, 1206, and 1222. In 1300 an eruption started about July 11 and lasted for 12 months with big earthquakes, tephra-fall, famine and human fatalities. The references of the annals to these eruptions are brief but to the point: A 1341 entry: 'Fire in Heklufell with a hard year and tephra-fall; many areas were abandoned. Darkness as great by day as by a winter night' (A. regii). - '..sheep and cattle died in Rangárvellir, and nearly five districts were ruined'. A 1389-90 entry: 'A fire started in Heklufell with such great force that the crash and a rumbling noise could be heard all over the country. Two farms, Skarð and Tjaldstaðir, were obliterated'. (Lögm. A.). The lava flow most likely engulfed both these farmsteads during this eruption.

The next Hekla eruptions occurred in 1510, 1597, and 1636. One of the most violent eruptions of Hekla began on February 13 1693. The tephra-fall was enormous, covering about 22,000 sq.km of land and ruining or badly damaging about 55 farms in neighbouring districts. The longest eruption of Hekla in historical times began on April 5 1766 and lasted until April 1768. The initial phase was violent with a very heavy tephra-fall, and later up to 18 columns of fire could be seen coming out of the mountain at the same time.

After this big eruption the Hekla took a rest for 77 years, but the next eruption started on September 2 1845. Very detailed information is available on this eruption. There was a considerable tephra-fall, and often there was a total darkness in the middle of the day in neighbouring districts. The eruption column could be seen from Reykjavik, and its height was measured to be 4370 m above the peak of Hekla. There was also a considerable lava-flow from the eruption, covering 25 sq.km of land, and on September 23 the farmstead Næfurholt was abandoned when the lava-flow came close to it through the ravine of a brook near by, inundating an area of cultivated grassland. The farm was moved after this eruption (see map on p. 174). There have also been several eruptions in the neighborhood of Hekla, including one in 1878 and another in 1913.

Four-wheel-drive vehicles can be driven across lava and tephra plains by the side of Lakagígar. Great care should be taken not to cause damage to this unique phenomenon of nature by driving vehicles up the fragile crater rims. The only way to explore the craters is to walk.

Lakagígar are now moss-covered in many places and in the hollows the moss gives way like a thick carpet. Craters and lava, however, are dominant landscape features here with red lava rocks and black cinders contributing to the profusion of colours. This picture was taken from the crater row just to the south-west of Laki. Here the fissure, which came into being in the 'Skaftá Fires' of 1783, continues its course up the mountain. The crater row reaches as high as the middle of the mountain side.

This is the only one of the Lakagígar craters which extends below the ground-water level. There is a clear-blue pond in the bottom surrounded by precipitous walls covered with reddish lava splashes. In between the lava formations the soft greyish-green moss is ubiquitous. From this crater enormous lava channels lie in southerly and easterly directions. Although they are now beautifully adorned with variegated vegetation, it is still easy to see that enormous quantities of lava were produced by this crater in 1783.

The lava from the Lakagígar (left) in an eruption of 1783, popularly called 'the Skaftá Fires', covers an area of 565 sq.km. It flowed down the river-beds of the Skaftá and the Hverfisfljót, radically changing their courses. Further down the lava engulfed anything that happened to be in its path, including pastures, homefields, grassland and human habitation. This is how the more westerly lava stream looks today. It is covered with a thick layer of moss, although it still clearly reveals traces of the cataclysmic upheaval which caused the lava to surge forward in this area almost two centuries ago.

Dimmuborgir (above) to the east of lake Mývatn is an area of most peculiar lava formations which owe their origin to a volcanic activity of great magnitude. A number of bushes grow between lava rocks of varying shapes with holes, hollows and openings. There are paths throughout this sanctuary, but many a visitor has lost his way in this labyrinth of shattered lava formations, making his stay here a little longer than originally planned.

Helgafell in Heimaey of the Vestmannaeyjar is one of the most beautiful volcanic cones in Iceland. The picture above shows Helgafell from the sea across Eiðið. The rock Heimaklettur is to the left and Klifið to the right. In fact Helgafell is considered an intermediary between two volcanic types, a cone and an eldborg, ('rock castle'). It is known to have erupted twice. In the former eruption an eldborg was built up in an effusive eruption, producing considerable lava, but the latter was a mixed eruption, giving birth to the cone which adorns Heimaey today. This latter eruption, however, occurred thousands of years before Iceland was settled and therefore Helgafell was not considered an active volcano.

Nevertheless a volcanic eruption started on January 23 1973, close to the south-eastern slopes of Helgafell, and a new volcano, called Eldfell, was built up (See pp. 190-214: Heimaey eruption 1973).

From Dyngjufjöll above Drekagil there is a beautiful view to Herðubreið (picture right). The dark stripes in the flat area show the main lava streams from the Askja eruption of 1961, when lava flowed from new craters near Öskjuop. Herðubreið is a table mountain. The volcanic eruptions which built up the table mountains are considered to have occurred under the ice-age glacier. The fires first melted a dome in the ice and then a hole up through it. The basalt magma which emerged underwent very sudden cooling in the melt-water, forming pillow lava and tephra which later turned into palagonite tuff. The enveloping glacier prevented the spread of the tephra with the result that the mountain grew higher and higher until it emerged from the surface of the water which had filled the opening in the glacier. In this way the mountain formed an insulating collar around the vent which enabled the volcanic activity to change from an explosive eruption to an effusive one with the production of lava which accumulated on top of the tuff socle.

As mentioned above, an eruption in Hekla itself started on March 29 1947 and continued for nearly 13 months. The eruption which started in, and close to, Hekla on May 5 1970 is described in a separate chapter (see pp. 174-179), and so is the Hekla eruption of 1980-81 (see pp.180-187), as well as the Hekla eruption in January 1991 (see pp.229-232).

More than half of the active volcanoes in Iceland are of the crater-row type, i.e. craters formed along a fissure, 35 km to 100 m long or even less. Craters on one and the same fissure may produce both tephra and lava. Lakagígar, for example, are such a composite crater-row.

Lava channels are quite common in Iceland. They occur in places where the lava originally flowed fast downhill along a kind of gully. Owing to the speed of the flow, little solidification takes place on the way. If the lava flow suddenly ceases at its source, the gully is emptied and the lava channels receive their present form. The picture on the right (p. 131) is of a newly-formed lava channel on Surtsey.

Above is a view from Herðubreiðarlindir over to Herðubreið. The table mountain form is quite clear, a belt of lava rocks at the top with palagonite tuff underneath (see text right on p.128). The pictures below were taken at the craters which came into being in the Askja eruption of 1961. It is a view in the direction of Herðubreið over the lava which flowed from Öskjuop and covered the old road to Askja. The craters still emit some smoke many years after the eruption.

The Lakagígar were formed in an eruption which began on Whit-Sunday, June 8 1783, and lasted until the beginning of February the following year. It is by far the biggest lava eruption on earth in historical times and possibly the biggest one after the ice age.

There is hardly any doubt that Lakagígar are one of the most impressive crater-rows that have been built up by a single fissure eruption. The detailed contemporary description of this eruption by the Reverend Jón Steingrímsson (the 'Fire Manuscript') is a reliable eye-witness account of the course of events during the Lakagígar eruption.

The fissure which opened up during the eruption is about 25 km long. It almost cuts through the 'móberg' (palagonite tuffs and breccias) mountain Laki, which is situated about the middle of the fissure. From the beginning on June 8 until July 29 1783 only the crater-row south-west of Laki was active and the lava flowed down the river-bed of the Skaftá, filling its canyon with lava masses. On July 29 the fissure north-east of Laki opened up and thereupon most of the lava flow followed the river-bed of Hverfisfljót.

The 1783 lava flow engulfed 2 churches and 13 farmsteads, and 30 other farms were badly damaged. The stunting of grass growth all over Iceland during the summer of 1783 was, however, far more disastrous. The main reason for the ruining of grass growth was the bluish haze caused by the enormous amount of volcanic gases released from the lava. This bluish haze lay all over the country and was even noticed in other European countries. Most likely it was mainly SO_2 gases which stunted the growth of grass. By comparison with the SO_2 gas percentage measured in the basaltic Surtsey magma it has been estimated that about 10 million tons of SO_2 gases were released during the Laki eruption.

The stunting of the grass and possibly also its fluor contamination from the tephra-fall caused a catastrophic starvation of livestock. During the resulting famine, the worst in Iceland's history, the population was reduced by nearly 24%. The main cause was the Lakagígar eruption, but the winter of 1783/84 was also very severe, ice and fire thus joining their destructive forces. No wonder that this was called the 'Haze Famine'.

The lava-flow from Lakagígar covers 565 km^2 of land, and its estimated volume is 12 km^3. The Lakagígar is one of the most extraordinary natural phenomena in Iceland. The craters are different in size and form, a mixture of explosive craters and lava-craters. Sometimes there are smaller craters on the slopes of bigger ones. This makes it hard to determine their exact number, which has been estimated to be around 100. The colours of the Lakagígar area are spectacular. There are black ash cones, red-burned scoria and lava, and moss-covered craters and lava streams.

It must be kept in mind, however, that this highland vegetation is very sensitive, and all nature lovers are very anxious to keep this virgin land of natural wonders unspoiled so that coming generations may also enjoy its beauty and marvel at the formidable power hidden underneath.

Explosive craters are common in Iceland, the youngest of them being Víti in the Askja volcano, which was formed in an explosive eruption on March 29 1875. Askja has erupted several times, last time in the autumn of 1961, when after more than 30 years of rest it gave birth to new hot springs on its surface, which were followed by a volcanic eruption that started on October 26 1961 and continued until the beginning of 1962.

On a map of Iceland made by Bishop Guðbrandur Þorláksson before 1585 the Hekla is shown to be violently active. It has the following comment: 'Hekla perpetuis damnata estib. et nivib. horrendo boatu lapides evomit', i.e. 'Hekla, which is cursed with eternal fires and snow, ejects rocks, making horrible noise'. The isolation of Iceland in the Middle Ages with vague news of Hekla eruptions reaching other European countries gave rise to the rumour that the entrance to Hell was to be found in Iceland and that black condemned souls could be seen hovering over Hekla.

nguitur limes inter utramq; mare

N DLEN
A FIOR
G.

Fiske-
notn.

Skabt a.

Hekla *perpetuis damnata estib. et niuib. horrendo boatu lapides evomit.*

Mydals Iokul.

Oddi

Eyafialla
Iokul.

Solheima
Iokul.

Breidaholst
stadar.

Medall

um
nic
vt

Surtsey, an island born in fire in 1963

A submarine eruption is in many ways similar to an eruption occurring underneath a glacier when melt-water is dammed up by the surrounding ice-sheet. When a volcanic fissure opens up on the sea-bed and the molten lava streams out, the cooling is rapid enough to change all the volcanic material immediately into scoria or tephra, building up a cone from the sea bed. Alternatively it is tossed up in the air and scattered over the surrounding area. Light tephra ash floats on the sea, but the gases from the magma are mixed with the steam column that rises from the boiling sea to considerable heights above the submarine volcano.

This is how the birth of a new island in the sea began at a depth of 130 m about 33 km from the Landeyjarsandur coastline and about 5.5 km WSW of Geirfuglasker, the nearest skerry of the Vestmannaeyjar archipelago, the southernmost spot of Iceland until then.

Eye-witness accounts of the birth of islands are very rare.

The new island, later known as Surtsey, is a notable exception. The fishing vessel Ísleifur II of the Vestmannaeyjar was fishing 4 miles west of Geirfuglasker the night before November 14 1963. At 6.30 in the morning the crew had finished to pay out the long line and went down to their quarters to have a cup of morning coffee. When they about 7 o'clock in the morning came up on deck again, they noticed a smell of sulphur, for which they could not find any reason. Shortly afterwards the sea around the ship unexpectedly became unquiet, and at daybreak within the next hour, they noticed an obscure mass rising out of the sea south-east of the vessel. They soon realized that black smoke clouds were rising out of the sea. This could only be a submarine eruption. The skipper called the Vestmannaeyjar radio station, reporting his observations, and sailed his ship nearer to the scene for a closer look. Half a mile away the sea was getting so rough that it was not felt safe to go any closer, and by that time they were quite sure what

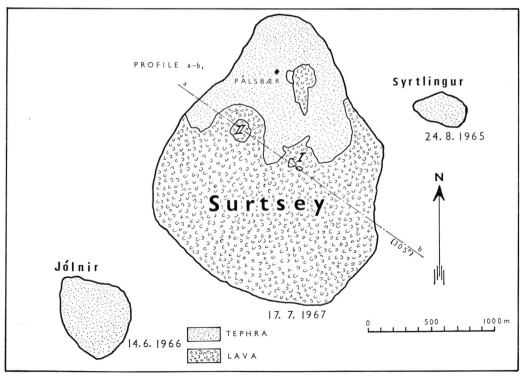

17. 7. 1967

TEPHRA
LAVA

The map shows the size of Surtsey on July 17 1967 and the islets of Syrtlingur and Jólnir on August 24 1965 and June 14 1966 respectively. Today there are only shallows where Syrtlingur and Jólnir used to be.

An eruption began in the sea in the morning of November 14 1963 just over 33 km off the Landeyjarsandur and only 23 km away from the town Vestmannaeyjar. The aerial view right was taken at 10.30 a.m. on November 16 1963. The height of the eruption column was then almost 9 km.

134

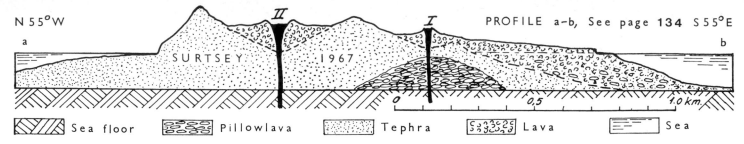

a   S U R T S E Y   1967   b

0   0.5   1.0 km.

Sea floor   Pillowlava   Tephra   Lava   Sea

This is a profile of Surtsey in 1967 after the two vents, known as Surtur II and Surtur I, had begun to erupt lava. This profile, shown as a-b on the map on p. 134, cuts through both the vents and therefore it lies approximately in the direction N 55°W to S 55°E. There is probably a socle of pillow lava around the Surtur I vent some distance towards the surface of the sea. Then tephra has accumulated on top of it, forming an island in the sea. The vent of Surtur II, on the other hand, was formed through the tephra layers that came from Surtur I, which at that time was close to reaching the surface of the sea. Therefore, there is probably no or very little pillow lava under Surtur II. A lava-producing effusive eruption began when the sea no longer found its way to the magma in the vent. Where lava flowed to the sea, layers of mixed tephra and lava were formed on the sea-bed, some of it, perhaps, appearing as pillow lava. Tephra or cinders is the raw material for palagonite tuff.

A view of Surtsey just after it emerged from the sea at 10.30 a.m. on November 16 1963. Aircraft were constantly encircling the eruption column. The Vestmannaeyjar and the south coast of Iceland are in the background.

was happening. Watching this new submarine eruption for some time, they felt that the activity was increasing and that the fissure was evidently lengthening during the time they stayed there.

The news of a volcanic activity in the sea soon spread and the first aircraft were encircling above the place at 10.30 a.m. Then the eruption was still gathering momentum. Stones were flying out of the black tephra column, which then had reached a height of 100 to 150 m. At the same time the eruption column grew steadily higher, and at 11 a.m. it had reached a height of about 4 km. The length of the fissure had then increased to about 400 m with four spots erupting simultaneously.

Expectedly, the direction of the fissure was near to the usual N35°E to S35°W found in the southern part of the country. Concentric waves could be seen coming from the volcanic area, and the sea nearest to the fissure had a peculiar brownish-green colour. Dark patches of floating tephra were drifting about and carried away by the wind. In the evening of that same day the coastguard vessel Albert came to the eruption area to determine its exact position. Then the waves started to break on shallows, and indicating that the fire ridge would soon break through the surface of the sea. The following night a new island was born.

This submarine eruption had shown very few precursory signs of what was going to happen so it was really quite unexpected. Although seismographs in Reykjavik had shown weak tremors the week before the eruption was first noticed, it was not possible with any certainty to determine their source. On Vestmannaeyjar and at Vík í Mýrdal on the coast of the mainland some sulphur smell was noted a few days

This is the crater-bowl of Surtur II (right), from which lava flowed intermittently from April 4 1964 to May 17 1965. The crater-bowl, however, varied a great deal in size and shape. Sometimes the lava overflowed the crater rims and at other times it flowed considerable distances through underground channels. Lethal gases hover over the crater. These are volatile substances released by the magma when it comes to the surface. One of the main substances in this blue haze, through which the sun barely penetrates, is sulphur dioxide in addition to water vapour. In the crater the lava boils and bubbles at a temperature of 1150°-1200° C.

before the eruption was first seen. The night before November 13 the trawler Þorsteinn Þorskabítur was engaged in fishery research to the south-west of Vestmannaeyjar when it was noticed that barely 4 km south-west of the place where the eruption started the temperature was 2.4° C higher within a limited area than in the surrounding sea. It can now be said that the weak tremors, the sulphur smell and the increased temperature in the sea indicate that the submarine eruption had started some time before it was noticed, but that it most likely had a slow start. It is probable, therefore, that warm vapour had been escaping from the volcanic area for some days before the crew of the fishing vessel Ísleifur II first witnessed the eruption.

As early as the second day after the eruption was first noticed the island had risen 10 m above sea level. Large amounts of volcanic material then piled up every day as the eruption was more or less continuous. The eruption column frequently reached a height of 9 km, making quite a threatening appearance to the citizens of Vestmannaeyjar, not least when it squirted volcanic ash with the help of the wind all over the islands. During the first few days of the eruption favourable weather made it easy to watch the growth of the island, both from the air and from the sea. On the third day the island had reached a height of about 40 m, but it was split from one end to the other. The sea, therefore, found its way into the vents during breaks in the explosions. The enormous amount of volcanic material, which in a matter of days built a mountain up to a height of 170 m measured from the sea floor, was very loose, consisting mostly of tephra. Hence it was easily washed away and re-shaped by the shifting action of ocean waves and the wind. The fire, however, was usually the strongest agent. The island continued to grow, and on November 20 it had reached a height of 70 m above sea level. Its length was then about 900 m and its width nearly 700 m. When the wind direction changed, the sea was blocked from reaching the vents on the lee-side, but soon the ocean waves broke into the vents from another side. Thus the demolishing forces of the ocean fought a violent battle with the creative forces of the volcanic eruption which were engaged in building up a new island, and in this struggle there were gains and losses on both sides. The craters on the island soon decreased in number, only one or two of them usually being active at a time. In general it can be said that there were explosive eruptions at irregular intervals when the sea was able to enter the craters, but as soon as a reef was formed that was big enough to keep the sea out, a continuous eruption started.

At night the Surtsey scene (left) often resembled a fireworks display. During the night before August 16 1964 the ocean breeze was cool, but the radiant heat from the crater Surtur II was comfortable. At short intervals there were explosions in the bubbling lava, causing red-hot splashes to fly high up in the air.

139

Above lava splashes fly out of one of the August vents of Surtur I. Below there is an aerial view of the area surrounding the crater-bowl of Surtur II, while no flowing lava can be seen on the surface.

It then became much more productive in building up the island as enormous amounts of tephra were then permanently ejected out of the crater, strengthening the crater walls. The flying bombs could then reach a height of about 2500 m. This eruption was not followed by any big noise. There was only a heavy roar when the eruption was most powerful and the bombs were falling on the sides of the crater or into the sea where they exploded. Thus the eruption continued to transport new material from the bowels of the earth up to the surface. The vents shifted from one place to another, the old took a rest and were soon replaced by new ones.

The island was officially baptized Surtsey after the giant Surtur of the old Eddaic poem Völuspá. At the end of March 1964 Surtsey was more than one km² in area, about 1100 m in width and 1400 m in length. Although the island thus had reached a considerable size, it was by no means thought it would be permanent because the winter storms had shown themselves to be most destructive, even in face of the enormous power of volcanic fire. The only hope for the survival of Surtsey was the supply of sufficient tephra material to stop sea-water from entering the vent, preventing its contact with the molten magma masses. This happened on April 4 1964, and from that date onwards the Surtsey eruption was very similar to one on land. By this time the wall between the crater and the sea had become very thick, so that an effusive eruption started by the crater being filled with red-hot lava from which glowing lava streams began to head for the sea. The intensity of the lava eruption fluctuated considerably, however. Sometimes the lava level in the crater subsided, but in between it overflowed the crater rims to such an extent that red-hot lava streams flowed down the tephra slopes, which were now gradually being covered with thin layers of lava. The result was a big lava dome, which by the end of April had reached a height of 90 m, the lava flow being very extensive at this time with many lava streams heading for the sea simultaneously. Where the lava met the sea huge columns of steam rose high up in the air. In places the lava was seen to flow red-hot along the sea-bed as if it were insulated from the water by enveloping steam. Therefore, the temperature of the sea rose substantially in these places. At other times the lava solidified very quickly, turning to scoria as soon as it came in contact with

Three lava vents appeared in a fissure that opened in Old Surtur (Surtur I) on August 19 1966, a crater which had not been active for 2 ¹/₂ years. The craters, which produced large amounts of lava, were called 'The August Vents'. The picture was taken in the evening of August 27 1966. Then lava flowed from two of the crater-cones. The volcanic island of Jólnir, which was first seen on December 26 1965, is in the background. Volcanic activity ceased there altogether about the middle of August 1966, and in the October of that same year Jólnir disappeared from the surface of the sea.

The first trips to Surtsey were made by sea. The conditions varied a great deal so that many of the early explorers got soaking wet when they landed on the island. Rubber dinghies were by far the most suitable means of transportation between the ships and the island. Some of them were propelled by oars while others were fitted with an outboard motor. Special skill was required for landing on the island when the sea was rough, and similarly great care was needed on departure from the island.

For a while the sandy beach of Surtsey could be used as a landing-strip for small aircraft after any bigger stones had been removed. Take-off was often rather difficult when the sand was too soft, limiting the number of passengers the aircraft could take. For a time Syrtlingur ruined all possibilities of landing on the island by its hot ash eruption. A helicopter was also used a few times for transportation between the vessels and the island or between Vestmannaeyjar Airport on Heimaey and Surtsey. This was the easiest mode of travel.

the sea. The sea-surge ground this material to glassy sand which then made up the beaches of Surtsey. At the end of April the surface flow of lava discontinued for a few months although the lava in the crater was constantly red-hot, molten and bubbling. During this period some lava apparently flowed through underground channels to the sea, strengthening the base of Surtsey. As soon as there was a pause in the lava flow to the sea, the sea-surge began to break down the edge of the lava. It was really quite surprising how soon sea-cliffs were formed and how big rocks lying on the beach turned into boulders rounded by the sea. All these rocks, however, helped to ward off the onslaughts by the ocean. When the lava resumed its flow from the crater on July 9 1964, it made its way over the old lava and fell off sea-cliffs formed by the sea-surge, but some of it travelled through underground channels and emerged through holes in the lower parts of the lava dome or down by the oldest sea-cliffs. Although the lava flow from the crater evidently varied a great deal, the amount of the flow during the first few months of the effusive eruption was very substantial, and it has been estimated that the bulk of volcanic solids produced was about the same in the explosive eruption as in the lava eruption up to the end of 1964.

On December 15 of that year the area of Surtsey was 213 hectares, 123 hectares of which were covered by lava. The lava flow discontinued for a while on May 17 1965, but about that time steam was seen to come out of the sea about 600 m ENE of Surtsey and by the end of May there were clear signs of a volcanic activity there with a new island in a state of birth. This new island had reached a height of 16 m and a diameter of 170 m by June 8. Four days later this island had gone, but it reappeared on June 14. Two days later the island had reached a height of 37 m and a length of 190 m and the name that was given to it was Syrtlingur ('Little Surtur'). On September 17 Syrtlingur reached its maximum height of 70 m, its length then being 650 m. After this date the Syrtlingur eruption became less and less active, whereas the demolishing action of the sea gained the upper hand with the result that it was seen for the last time on October 17 1965.

On December 26 1965 a volcanic activity was noticed about 900 m south-west of Surtsey, and on January 2 a new island emerged there with two active vents. It disappeared, however, within a few days. Thus, this new island emerged

At the end of May 1965 a volcanic activity began in the sea about 600 m ENE of Surtsey, giving birth to the island of Syrtlingur, which reached a height of 70 m and a length of 650 m. The above picture is of the hot ash eruption of Syrtlingur on July 3 1965 as it was seen from Surtsey. Below is an aerial view of the volcanic island of Jólnir, taken on May 24 1966.

Syrtlingur (right) was continuously active on most of July 3 1965 while material for the foundations of Pálsbær, the hut of the Surtsey Research Society, was being taken ashore. The first foundations were set down in the Surtsey lava right opposite Syrtlingur, which then buried them in a thick layer of ashes so that a new site had to be selected in a sandy area near the lagoon, where Pálsbær was situated until a new research hut, Nýibær, was erected in 1988 (see p.167).

Jólnir was violently active on May 24 1966 when this picture was taken from a ship. When the sea gets into direct contact with the magma, the latter disintergrates with cinders flying up in the air. This is the so-called hot ash eruption.

When a vent emits lava which turns into hard rock through slow solidification, it is called an effusive eruption. A brook of water digs a channel in the ground with banks of varying height. A stream of lava, on the other hand, often builds up a ridge underneath its course with lava flowing off on both sides as can be seen in the picture to the right.

144

and submerged again and again until April 7 when it vanished for the 5th time, but once again it reappeared on April 14, and on May 12 it had again grown to a length of 560 m and a height of 40 m. The eruption column was more than 6000 m high on May 20, when the first landing on this island took place. About this time it received the name Jólnir (Jól = Christmas) because it had first been seen on Boxing Day. Jólnir was visited again on May 24 (see pictures on p. 146) when the visitors reached the foot of the crater cone that had developed on the southern part of the island. At the beginning of August the Jólnir eruption began to decline very sharply and ceased altogether by the middle of the month. But the sea-surge continued its activity and in October Jólnir disappeared for good after an intermittent existence for 10 months. Its maximum size had been an area of 28 hectares and a height of 70 m.

Let us now revert to Surtsey. In the morning of 19 August 1966 a fissure opened in the crater called Old Surtur (marked I on the map on p. 134), which had then been dormant for 2¹/₂ years, i.e. since the end of January 1964. This fissure was about 220 m long and 7-15 m wide, emitting a 100 m wide lava stream which headed for the sea. Subsequently three lava cones developed on this fissure, two of which adjoined, whereas the third was situated at some distance from the others. These vents, which produced very large quantities of lava, were referred to as 'the August Vents.' On August 21 the lava flow was estimated to be 5-10 m³/sec at a short distance from the vent. During this period continuous tremors were felt on Surtsey. They were particularly noticeable inside the hut which had been erected (Pálsbær). The lava flow from the August Vents continued right until the end of 1966, bringing radical changes to the Surtsey landscape. For instance, the lava inundated a site on the eastern part of the island which had been chosen for the Surtsey hut before Syrtlingur began its activity 600 m off the shore, burying the site in a thick layer of ashes, which, however, had been washed away by the sea-surge by the time the site was engulfed by the lava from the August Vents. But on January 1 1967 it was noticed that a fissure had opened up on the north side of the crater wall of Surtur I, from which lava flowed into the lagoon in front of Pálsbær (see pictures on p. 155). The next day the lava had more than half-filled the lagoon and there was some anxiety for the safety

The first landing on Jólnir took place on May 20 1966. These pictures show the second landing there on May 24. Below is the rubber dinghy used for the landing with Surtsey in the background. The picture above was taken at the foot of the crater cone on the southern end of the island. Drizzling rain mixed with the tephra-fall from the eruption. Volcanic bombs were falling far and wide. Several of them were the size of a man's fist, and some even as big as 80 cm in diameter.

Often the Surtsey lava flowed long distances underground and sometimes did not emerge to the surface until it had reached as far as the seashore. Yet openings were sometimes found in the roof of the channel, through which the rapid stream of the red-hot lava could be studied. The temperature of the lava in these underground channels was apparently similar to that of the lava in the crater, i.e. 1150-1160° C. Therefore, the heat radiating from it was enormous.

No flowing surface lava could be seen near the vents of Old Surtur (Surtur I) on May 19 1967, but then lava flowed along underground channels to openings near the sea-shore where jets of steam could be seen rising in the air. The vents were very hot, and it was very hard to climb the crater cones because of noxious gases from the magma.

In the picture on the right, taken on August 29 1966, a lava-fall is seen to flow off older sea-cliffs formed by the sea-surge after the first lava flow on Surtsey. The lava stream transports solidified lava junks just as ordinary rivers bring down ice floes.

A lava stream (above) is issuing from the crater in the background down over older lava on August 29 1966. The lava stream often changes its course as the lava piles up, filling up older fissures and hollows.

Sometimes the precipitations on Surtsey were colourful beyond description (right): They were orange, yellow-green, red, yellow-orange and sometimes bluish. The lava assumed these colours from the condensation of gases which escaped from holes and cracks in the lava.

150

Precipitations in the lava below Old Surtur (Surtur I) were most colourful. From a distance the lava often looked as if it were covered with moss. The yellow green colour derives from sodium and potassium sulphates, but other sulphates and pure sulpur also led to precipitations.

152

Here new lava inundates older lava-flows which have already been coloured by precipitations. The new lava advances inside a semi-hardened crust as if it rolled forward in a bag.

Constantly, however, redhot embers can be seen in the lava, and sometimes the crust bursts, releasing a thinner material until that, too, has developed an enveloping crust.

of Pálsbær. Such worries were needless, however, because at this time a fissure had opened on the inside of the crater wall. Already on January 3 more lava was flowing from it than from the north side where the lava flow stopped altogether on January 5 when the edge of the lava was at a distance of 120 m from Pálsbær.

From the beginning of January until June 5 1967 the lava flow from the August Vents in Surtur I was continuous, one of the vents being most productive, however. Yet the lava flow was clearly on the wane and much of it passed through underground channels down to the sea-shore.

On June 5 1967 flowing lava on Surtsey was seen for the last time. If we look upon that date as the last day of the Surtsey eruption, it had lasted for three years and almost seven months. By that time it had become Iceland´s second longest eruption in historical time, only a few months shorter than the 'Myvatn Fires' of 1725-1729. These eruptions behaved similarly in many ways, even though one of them started on the sea-bed and the other in the highlands. When the Surtsey eruption ceased, the new island was 2.8 km² in area.

To the left embers can be seen in a crack in the Surtsey lava, its edges being adorned with variegated precipitations. In the top right-hand picture scientists are at work, measuring the temperature of a lava stream. To the right is Pálsbær and the lagoon before and after the lava flow of January 1967, which halted its advance 120 m away from Pálsbær. - The above picture shows an experiment that is being made with a lava stream. Sea-water is pumped onto it to cool it on one side in an attempt to change its course by creating a solidified barrier out of the molten lava. This method was later used during the Heimaey eruption of 1973 on a bigger scale to save the town of Vestmannaeyjar (see p.201).

155

The point was aptly made by one of the geologists at work on the island when he commented to the effect that a big disadvantage of islands was the fact that they were surrounded by the sea. In the past only few geologists were used to having to practise seamanship along with their research work.

The Surtsey Society was founded for the purpose of organizing the co-operation of scientists and planning the whole body of Surtsey research. Originally only a committee was set up to assist Icelandic geologists in their Surtsey studies. Soon, however, great interest of overseas scientists in an active participation in these studies became manifest and the role of the Surtsey Society is now an overall co-ordination and planning of all Surtsey research. The Society has already published nine books, 'Surtsey Research Progress Reports', and held several meetings and two conferences in Reykjavik on the Surtsey research effort. The first conference was held in 1965, devoting almost all its time to biological studies, but the interest of biologists increased greatly after the lava flow began on April 4 1964 because after that the survival of Surtsey was more or less secure. The second conference was held in 1967, dealing with both biological and geological topics in addition to many specialized branches of each.

Hardly any other Icelandic eruption has been studied more assiduously than the Surtsey one. This research still goes on even though no lava flows there any more. The history of the eruption has been meticulously recorded right from its beginning, and data collection was carried out on the island both during the eruption and after it ceased.

This work will be continued for years to come because this island presents a unique opportunity for a study of the genesis of land right from its throes of birth as well as of its formative history, the chief agents of which are the sea-surge, rain, the sun and the wind. Of particular interest are the biological aspects of these studies: How does life start on an island born of fire in the middle of the sea? These studies, however, have been made under difficult conditions.

A number of lava streams (above) were flowing parallel to the Surtsey sea-shore on January 7 1967. Frequently a steam-cloud covered large areas of the shore.

The red-hot lava (right) drops into the foaming sea-surge on the Surtsey shore. Every backward flow of the surf revealed the red-hot lava stream, whereas on its return all the scene disappeared in a steam-cloud.

156

This surf is no different from that of any other ocean shore. But these cliffs and this sandy beach are only a few years old because this picture was taken on Surtsey on May 20 1967 with a view towards the Vestmannaeyjar. The history of the development of Surtsey, which emerged from the sea from a depth of 130 m in one more or less continuous eruption, is very instructive for students of rare natural phenomena. No less interesting is the formative history of this new island. The sea with its breakers and currents, the rain and the wind are constantly busy transforming and moulding it. Their demolishing action is surprisingly effective. The best evidence of this is the speed with which the islands of Syrtlingur and Jólnir were swept away shortly after the volcanic activity ceased. Nobody dared to predict a permanent existence for Surtsey until an effusive eruption started, producing lava as a result of the slower cooling of the magma. Even the edge of the lava, which formed sloping lava flows down to the sea, has now been broken down by the surf and turned into precipitous sea-cliffs, skirted by a rock-strewn sandy beach. These rocks no longer resemble chunks of recent lava. Instead there are sea-worn boulders and gravel banks between areas of finer sand. Many people would consider the age of this land to be thousands of years. So much does the swift and decisive action of the forces of nature confuse our sense of time.

The colours of the precipitations on Surtsey presented a marvelous spectacle, but they soon faded and completely disappeared in due course. This is a view from Surtsey to the Vestmannaeyjar and the mainland on January 9 1967, with Mýrdalsjökull and Eyjafjallajökull in the background. Lava is still flowing into the sea as can be seen by the steam-cloud.

158

The Surtsey research effort is financially supported by the Icelandic government and Icelandic research funds, but in addition it has received generous grants from various overseas research funds as Surtsey is considered a unique field for some specialized research. In historical time only very few islands on earth have been known to be born of volcanic activity and become permanent geographical features. Up to now those few occasions have given little or no spur at all to scientific evolutionary research. Even when all life on the island of Krakatoa was eradicated in a volcanic eruption in 1883, hardly any research was done on the subsequent re-settlement of vegetation on the island. When the first biologist came to the island three years later, he found that 30 plants had already taken root there, and ten years later the whole island was covered by trees, including palm-trees, and other plants. A more detailed study was made of the Island of Ana-Krakatoa, but owing to much more favorable climatic conditions and the luxuriant vegetation on neighboring islands it can hardly be compared with Surtsey, which is surrounded by the icy breakers of the North-Atlantic. The sea-surge washes its entire shore and projects its spray over the whole island. When the weather is rough, the wind churns up the salty tephra, and when Syrtlingur and Jólnir were in their prime, they covered Surtsey with ashes, stifling any bud which attempted settlement on the island. Owing to the biological research work, Surtsey has been made a sanctuary under the control of the Surtsey Research Society.

Evidently it will take a long time for vegetation to take root on the island. Nature is in no hurry. For the research effort this slow development is favorable, giving the researchers plenty of time to study every detail that might throw a new light on the origin of life in a sterile environment. Plant parts and seeds from neighbouring islands have been washed ashore and some beach plants have managed to take root in the upper parts of sandy beaches. In the upper parts of Surtsey seeds of plants have most likely been brought from neighbouring islands by birds. The colonisation of plants on Surtsey is discussed further on pp.172-173. Sea birds have now for many years nested on Surtsey. (see p.171).

While ornithologists and botanists keep a watchful eye on any developments on land, oceanographers, marine biologists and algologists are busy studying the sea around Surtsey, its submarine base and the sea-shore. Migratory birds that call at Surtsey on their way from more southern lands have been studied to find out about the growth potential of seeds brought by them.

An interesting subject for comparative study is vegetation on nunataks. Although the relationship between the two may not seem obvious, such glacier rocks are to some extent analogous to a volcanic island in the sea. To both, plants have to be carried a long way over areas that are barren and lifeless in respect of vegetation. Therefore, the botanical research

that has been carried out in recent years in Esjufjöll of the Vatnajökull glacier (see map on p.52 and picture on p.82) has been given considerable attention by those who are studying the formation of soil and vegetation on Surtsey, where samples of volcanic cinders are collected for the study of the development of their soil potential for plants.

An important geological aspect of the Surtsey research work has been detailed recording of the history of the eruption from its inception to its final phase to make the development of all its main factors accessible. The history of older eruptions in Iceland was recorded either by eye-witnesses or on the basis of second-hand accounts. Thus eyes and ears were the chief sources of information for the early annalists, some of their works giving a very clear account of the chain of events. Even today the eyes and ears of an observant spectator are very important research tools. Photographs of course, preserve the visual side of an eruption better than any human brain or even a detailed description. A photograph might even preserve an event that lasted only a fraction of a second, an event that might be unique and difficult to describe in words or explain satisfactorily. The recording of the history of an eruption, however, is not the only geological aspect of the research work. By measuring the quantity of the volcanic material produced within each period and by geochemical and geophysical research certain facts may be discovered which form a much more reliable basis for any general conclusions.

Since the beginning of volcanic studies it has been clear that various gases are brought to the surface with the magma (see p.121) and there has been great interest in an identification of the highly noxious gases which appear in the form of a bluish haze. The first attempt to collect samples of such gases was apparently made at Hekla in 1846, the summer after it erupted. The result was disappointing because a chemical analysis of the samples revealed mainly atmosphere, carbon dioxide and water. The first successful attempts to collect gases from a volcanic crater were made on Hawaii, and some measure of success has also been achieved along the same lines at Nyiragongo in Africa and on Stromboli. After the Hekla eruption of 1947-48 and the Askja eruption of 1961 some attempts at gas collection from lava fissures and steamholes were made, but the samples again turned out to consist largely of atmosphere mixed with carbon dioxide. In 1964 many attempts were made at collecting volcanic gases on Surtsey, both from red-hot lava fissures where the temperature was 800° C and from the main crater where the temperature was about 1200 °C. At first many of the attempts were unsuccessful. Some of the instruments could not withstand the temperature, but others simply dissolved in acid vapours. Finally, however, a place in the Surtsey lava was discovered which had some unique characteristics that were favorable for the collection of gas samples. Then the lava flowed from the crater through a big subterranean channel, but in one place there was a narrow slit in the roof of the channel through which gas streamed out at great speed. As the gas escaped from the slit it caught fire so that a narrow flame stood out of the hole in the lava. An attempt was made to measure the temperature by means of an electric thermometer housed in an iron cylinder, but the flame melted the iron in an instant and ruined the thermometer. Thus the temperature must have exceeded 1300 °C. Here some gas samples could be captured and fed to collection containers through a stainless steel pipe by means of its own pressure. A chemical analysis of this gas showed that it was entirely uncontaminated by the atmosphere, so this is possibly the best sample that has been retrieved from a volcanic area up to now. Water vapour proved to be 80% of its content, and apart from water the gas consisted of sulphur dioxide (SO_2), hydrogen and carbon dioxide with small amounts of carbon monoxide, nitrogen and argon in addition to some hydrogen chloride and sulphuric vapour.

Constantly chemical research has been made into the nature of the loose volcanic material and the lava produced by the Surtsey eruption. As might be expected there is no chemical difference between the tephra and the lava. Rapid cooling of the magma causes the formation of tephra whereas slow cooling results in the formation of lava. These studies have also revealed that the Surtsey lava is totally different from those of Askja and Hekla. It is more similar to volcanic materials from Katla and Eldgjá, although there are some differences. Volcanologists have concluded on the basis of this evidence that Surtsey does not derive from a magma reservoir which is shared by any volcano on the mainland of Iceland. It was mentioned above (see p.134) that a submarine eruption has some similarities to a subglacial one, and the Surtsey eruption has shown without any doubt that it is water coming from outside which causes the magma to disintegrate with the resulting tephra being flung high up in the air. On page 128 it is mentioned that the table mountain Herðubreið was formed by a volcanic eruption underneath an ice-age glacier. If the sea around Surtsey disappeared, we would see a mountain that looked very much like table mountains, but in time the volcanic tephra turns to palagonite tuff, although it has not been known until now how long such a development takes. Possibly the research on Surtsey will be of great value in this connection.

Resting on the tuff base of Surtsey is the lava shield produced by the effusive eruption. According to the table mountain theory the chain of events leading to the formation of both Surtsey in the sea and Herðubreið and other table mountains on land is as follows: The first magma flowing out of a volcanic fissure in the sea or underneath a thick glacier turns to pillow lava, which has a vitreous crust over a crystallized rock interior. The surrounding water or sea absorbs all vapours and other combustible materials so that there are no explosions owing to the overwhelming pressure of the water. So far no eruption has found its way to the surface of the glacier or the sea. The glacier melts from underneath and a pile of pillow lava rises into an ice dome full of water (or from the sea-bed in the case of a submarine eruption). Finally, the pressure from above can no longer withstand the internal pressure of the volcanic gases, and the result is a violent explosive eruption. Then the issuing magma changes to cinders or tephra owing to rapid cooling. The explosive eruption piles up tephra on top of the pillow lava, a raw material for palagonite tuff. If the explosive eruption lasts long enough for the volcanic material to break through the surface of the ice cap (or the sea), there will be a continuous hot ash eruption, followed by an effusive eruption with a lava flow if the tephra succeeds in preventing water (or seawater) from reaching the magma on its way to the surface. So far it has not been possible to determine whether there is pillow lava under the Surtsey socle, and it would in any case be very deep down. A core drill was used for research on Surtsey in July 1979. The drillings provided however no evidence of pillow lava, see p. 170.

Geophysical studies of the Surtsey eruption have been concerned with various of its aspects. The emission speed of the volcanic material from the Surtsey vents was measured and found to be 150-200 m/sec and the eruption column reached a height of 9 km when the conditions in the upper layers of the atmosphere were favourable. Lightning flashes appeared in the eruption column during the first few months of the eruption. Many aspects of its influence on the surrounding sea were studied. If half the energy generated by the eruption had been spent on heating up the ocean, it would have raised the temperature of one km^3 of sea by 2° C. As the depth of the sea is only 130 m near Surtsey we might have expected a measurable increase in temperature over a large area, but that was not the case. The tephra apparently acted as an effective insulator between the magma and the sea with the result that the eruption released much more heat to the atmosphere than to the sea.

Geomagnetic measurements were made both from the air and on the island itself. It was found that the magnetic field of the lava is highly anomalous, whereas the field of the tephra areas is very homogeneous, the tephra being about 100 times less magnetized than the lava.

Special seismographic measurements were made on the occasion of the Surtsey eruption in addition to measurements made by permanent seismographs located on the mainland. In general the earth is quiet during a lava-producing eruption, but earthquakes are more liable to occur during explosive eruptions. The tremors were sharpest when the eruption was moving from one vent to another on Surtsey itself or from Surtsey to Syrtlingur. The temperature of the lava in the crater was measured by inserting a 10 m long chromel-almud thermocouple into the magma and keeping it there until the voltmeter ceased to rise. This took no more than a minute, but during this time so much lava had accumulated on the ther-

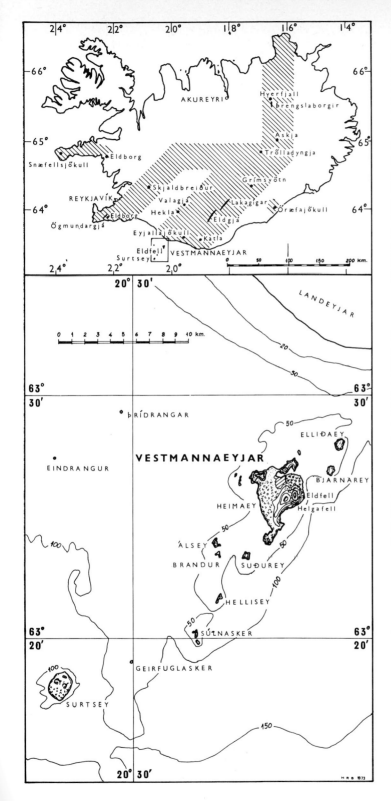

mocouple that two men had difficulties in retrieving it. Two measurements were made in this way, but it was found inadvisable to carry them out more often owing to the risks involved. The measurements recorded the temperatures of 1150°C and 1160°C respectively, so it is thought likely that the temperature of the magma flowing to the crater was 1150-1200 °C.

It is not possible to give a more detailed account here of the research carried out on Surtsey, in which a number of scientists were actively engaged. Many tasks still need to be done even though the eruption has ceased. The genesis of this fire island has been told to some extent here in words and pictures, but its formative history lies largely in the future, which will reveal Nature's pleasure of dressing it with vegetation and adorning it with animals. In Surtsey Nature has presented us with a research station to enable us to increase our knowledge of various factors of geological history and of life on earth.

There have been lava eruptions in every century of Icelandic history so they are well-known to all Icelanders. In many parts of the country there are relatively young and bare lava fields which show quite clearly where the flow came from and how it behaved, e.g. whether it was viscous and slow-moving or thin as a soup and fast-moving. There are lava channels, rough black lava and undulating lava fields, lava craters and explosive craters of countless dimensions and types, upright lava rocks and caves.

The variety of lava formations is virtually infinite, and a close examination may reveal many aspects of their origin. To witness a flow of glowing lava is a unique experience as it presents a live demonstration of the creation of the many different lava formations. After an effusive eruption started on Surtsey the volcanic activity behaved very much like an eruption on land.

In the top of the map volcanic areas that have been active since the last ice-age are indicated by shading, some of the volcanoes being indicated by name. Most of the volcanic areas are within a wide belt lying askew across the centre of the country from south-west to north-east. Outside this belt, however, are Snæfellsnes and Öræfajökull. All this volcanic area is approximately 35.000 km². For further information on the volcanic areas and volcanoes. (See also p.120).
The lower map shows the location of Surtsey in relation to Vestmannaeyjar and the mainland. On the Island of Heimaey is shown the old volcano Helgafell, and the new one, Eldfell, which was built up in the Heimaey eruption of 1973. (See pp. 190-214).

161

One point, however, made this fire island extraordinary: It was the interplay of the forces of fire and those of the sea. The variety of this spectacle made it fascinating to watch for long periods at a time. When the lava flow was in spate, a wide lava stream might pour in the sea and it could be seen advancing long distances along the sea-bed. When the flow was less forceful, it rolled into the sea inside fragile pockets of solidified lava, and from time to time small rifts opened with glowing lava rivulets plunging into the sea-surge. It was interesting to watch how the lava streams sometimes turned a sharp corner to the side when they approached the sea as if they shrank from contact with the water. This happened quite frequently when the flow was not particularly fast-moving. Then the cooling was quickest in the part of the lava stream which was closest to the sea with the result that a dam of solidified lava might be piled up along the sea-shore.

This observation was the basis of the idea to try to change the course of a lava-rivulet by pumping sea-water and cooling it down on one side to build a dam from the lava itself. Such experiment was made in Surtsey (see p. 155), and the experience gained was used on a bigger scale during the Heimaey eruption of 1973 to protect the harbour- entrance and the town of Vestmannaeyjar against the engulfing lava-flow. (see p. 201).

On Surtsey it was also observed, however, that sometimes openings developed in this dam on the sea-side of the lava-stream, through which the lava found its way to the sea. Then big jets of steam rose from the sea as the red-hot lava tongue disintegrated to glassy cinders which later formed the sandy beaches of Surtsey.

The lava could be crossed on foot, even if it was considerably hot, because an insulating crust soon developed. Often, however, it floated on redhot liquid lava underneath. In many places, however, it was impossible to stand still on this lava crust, and rucksacks or other luggage could not be put down without a risk of damage.

Before Pálsbær, the hut of the Surtsey Research Society, was built, visitors to Surtsey stayed in tents. The conditions radically changed with the advent of Pálsbær, both in respect of sleeping-quarters and storage facilities for instruments, cameras etc. When a weary visitor to Surtsey lay down to sleep at night after a tour of this extraordinary island, he could not help marvelling at the enormity of the natural forces which created it. In the October of 1963 there was no land here. Now we have a sandy beach strewn with sea-worn boulders which even the most competent geologists might think were many hundreds of years old if they did not know their origin. Here we have seacliffs which look like ancient rock-formations.

Eruptions have taken place off the Icelandic coast before in historical time. In the annals for 1211 it is stated that Sörli Kolsson discovered 'The New Fire Islands', whereas the old ones, which had been there from time immemorial, had disappeared. Thus it is indicated that some islands emerged off the Icelandic coast in 1211 and at the same time some other islands vanished. The name of the ones which disappeared indicates that they, too, were of volcanic origin. No doubt this volcanism occurred on the submarine ridge which extends south-westwards from the Reykjanes Peninsula along the whole length of the Atlantic towards the Antarctic and northwards from Iceland to Jan Mayen. Volcanic eruptions off the Reykjanes Peninsula are referred to in annals for the years 1226, 1231, 1238, 1240, 1422, and 1583. Finally, there is a reliable source on, and an eye-witness account of, an eruption off the Reykjanes Peninsula in the spring of 1783. A ship arrived on the scene when an island had emerged from the sea. The captain made a sketch of the island which looks very much like Surtsey as it was in the initial phase of the eruption. This island was called Nýey ('New Island'), but when it was to be dedicated to King Christian VII with a stone bearing his initials and the appropriate date, the island had been engulfed by the sea again. But Surtsey is definitely there to stay.

The lava still emits some heat, but in winter it is occasionally covered with snow. Nobody who now flies over the Vestmannaeyjar archipelago is able to discern that one of these islands was born of fire only a few years ago.

One of the most remarkable phenomena of the Surtsey eruption was the red-hot lava flowing into the sea. Sometimes the lava surged forward inside a solidified lava crust which now and then burst open with the result that the sea came in direct contact with the molten lava. Then there were sometimes great explosions which ejected lava splashes high up in the air.

There is still considerable heat under the Surtsey lava (right) even though the surface is cold enough for snow to stay on the ground. The picture above of Surtsey with the Vestmannaeyjar in the background was taken on February 8 1970. The picture is certainly symbolic for the whole of Iceland, a land of ice and fire. Underneath snow and glacial firn there is fire. Great are the contrasts of Icelandic nature.

164

SURTSEY
16. 11. 1963.

SURTSEY, its creation and erosion.

As has been related above the creation of the volcanic island of Surtsey started when an eruption began on the ocean floor on November 14 1963, at a depth of 130 m. Already on November 16, when the picture on the left was taken from an airplane, the volcanic oblong ridge of cinders had reached a height of more than 10 m above sea level, split by a fissure, which was flooded by the sea. Separate vents were erupting at the same time, but shifting from one end of the fissure to the other. Later on the island became nearly circular, and then only one crater was active most of the time. Thus a new island was born, 33 km from the south coast of Iceland, and 5,5 km WSW of the nearest skerry of the Vestmannaeyjar archipelago. During the first days the eruption column reached a height of about 9 km. When a volcanic rift opens on the ocean floor, the lava immediately changes to tephra, which builds up on the ocean floor or is thrown up in the air. Ocean waves washed away much of the loose volcanic material, but as the eruption continued Surtsey had become 1100 m wide and 1400 m long by the end of March 1964.

On April 4 1964, glowing lava started to stream up through one crater, called Surtur I, without being cooled off by the water. Only then was it thought to be safe to predict a long future for the island. Later on another crater, Surtur II also became active and soon took over from Surtur I. On August 19 1966 a 220 m long fissure opened up on the floor of the older Surtur I crater. From the craters on this fissure, the so-called August craters, considerable lava flowed until June 5 1967, when a moving lava glow was seen for the last time. The Surtsey eruption is, therefore, considered to have come to an end that day. Then the total area of Surtsey above sea level was about 2.8 km^2. The total volume of tephra and lava produced in the Surtsey eruption has been estimated to be about 1.1 km^3. It had lasted for almost 3 years and 7 months.

But that was not the end of the creation of Surtsey. Subterranean heat and moisture have transformed ash into hard tuff, and the surf has broken up and changed the shoreline of Surtsey. This coastal erosion is evident on the vertical air photographs taken at intervals by Landmælingar Islands, (The Icelandic Survey Dep.) The picture on the left was taken during the summer of 1969.

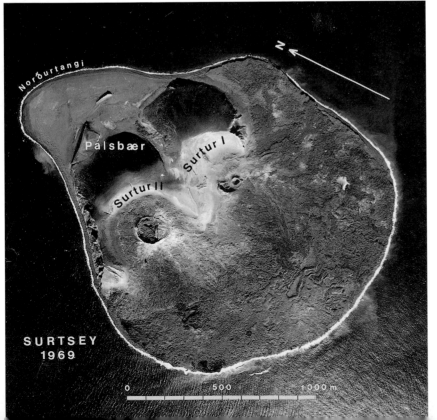

Norðurtangi

Pálsbær

Surtur I

Surtur II

N

SURTSEY
1969

0   500   1000 m

166

The vertical photograph (right) was taken by Landmælingar Íslands (The Icelandic Survey Department) in 1979, about 12 years after the Surtsey eruption ended, and 10 years after the lower picture on p. 166 was taken. The picture on the right below was taken in 1988.

By comparing the three aerial pictures, taken in 1969, 1979 and 1988 several features stand out. During these years the ocean surf shaped Surtsey considerably and also reduced its size. It was mentioned above that layers of lava flow covered large areas of the scoria or tephra which built the foundation of the island from the sea bed up to and above sea level. When the lava flow started it was generally considered certain that the hard lava rock would withstand the erosive action of the ocean waves better than the loose volcanic material. This was true of the first years of the young Surtsey, but it took a much shorter time than expected for the sub-terranean heat and the moisture in the ash to transform it into hard and compact tuff. On the other hand the relentless marine erosion has led to undercutting of the lava layers, mainly in heavy winter storms, followed by collapse of the layers above. In this way the whole cliff-face of lava recedes along the south-western coast, and in front of it a platform, serrated by ocean waves, comes into being, a sandy beach strewn with big rock fragments of lava. They very soon become rounded boulders which, by the action of waves and currents, are carried along the coast-line in a semi-horizontal see-sawing movement. This is how Norðurtangi (Northern Ness) became covered with boulders of lava even though this part of the island was never visited by a lava flow. The rapid erosion of these lava cliffs has produced the large amounts of boulders needed to protect the high tephra cliff of the crater rim of Surtur II. In the meantime the tephra has been growing harder and thereby more fit to withstand attacks by the erosive forces.

A core drill was used for the research on the tuff of Surtsey in June-August 1979. The site of the drilling is marked in the picture on the right above. It is about 58 m above sea level, near the edge of the main crater (Surtur I).

In the aerial picture at right is shown the site of the New Research Hut, Nýibær. The shore has come close to the site of the older research hut, Pálsbær.

167

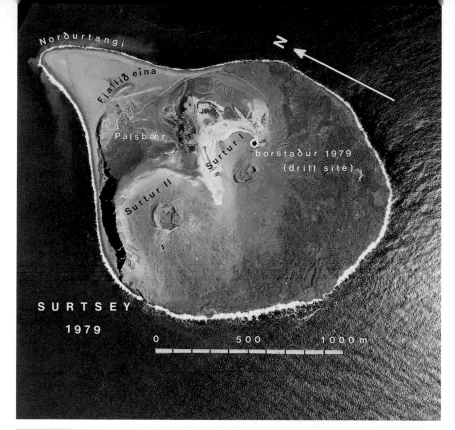

SURTSEY
1979

0   500   1000 m

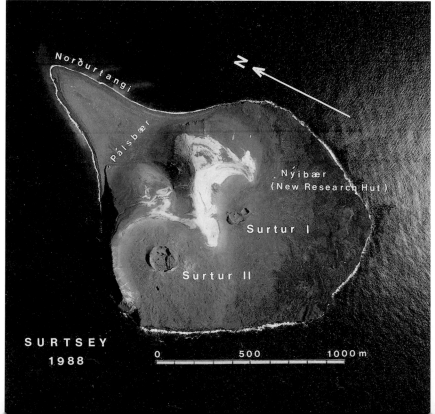

SURTSEY
1988

0   500   1000 m

The development of the Surtsey coastline has been followed with great interest, as mentioned above in relation to the aerial photographs on pp. 166-167. The picture on the left is a view of the coastline on the southern part of the island where the lava cliff-face has been receding about 20 m a year, during the post-volcanic period of 1967-75. The total annual loss of the surface area of Surtsey has been about 7.5 hectares during the same period. In the years after 1975 the annual loss has been only half that, which might indicate some stabilization of the cliff areas.

Below the lava cliffs there is a terrace strewn with boulders. The almost unbroken storm waves are breaking rocks from the lava cliffs, and the waves and current action transforms them from sharp-edged rocks into rounded boulders, and transports them along the coastline towards the northern part of the island.

The lower picture on the left is a view of the boulder terrace below the tephra cliff, of the crater Surtur II (see p.167). The tephra is here more or less hardened into tuff, and is rather well protected from the ocean waves by the boulder terrace, the origin of which is the lava rocks further south.

The picture on the right (p. 169) is a view over the boulders which have been carried by ocean waves all the way to Northern Ness (Norðurtangi) from the cliffs of the lava area. This promontory was formed chiefly from gravel and sand by the action of waves and currents. The western beach is covered with boulders, as shown in the picture on the right. As the Northern Ness is built by wave action, its position can shift somewhat, depending on the variation of heavy storms and currents.

168

After the end of the Surtsey eruption the lava and the tephra still contained a great deal of heat, which in conjunction with moisture transformed the tephra into hard tuff much more quickly than had been expected. In June-August 1979 a core drilling was performed for research on the hydrothermal processes and the formation of tuff. Drilling took place at a spot about 58 m above sea level (see picture above, and the vertical aerial photograph top right on page 167).

The heat in the borehole soon exceeded 100° C. Under the surface loose volcanic materials had been fused in time by the heat into a more solid rock. Below is a sample of the core from a depth of 71.9 m below the surface, and on the right a sample of the core from a depth of 150.2 m. Here the tuff is slightly altered, unlayered and compact. This spot is 42 m above the original ocean floor.

The drilling showed no evidence of pillow lava formation, but provided information on tuff formations and submarine as well as sub-glacial eruptions.

Seabirds were most likely the first living creatures to land on Surtsey, even before the first man set foot on the new island. Already during intervals between eruptions various species of seabirds frequently rested on the island. The most important ornithological event happening on Surtsey was in 1970 when the first two species of birds were found to be nesting on the island: the Fulmar *(Fulmarus glacialis)* and the Black Guillemot *(Cepphus grylle)*. One pair of each species then nested successfully. Now in 1990 six species nest regularly on Surtsey. Besides the Fulmar and Black Guille-mot they are: Kittiwake *(Rissa tridactyla)*, Herring Gull *(Larus argentatus)*, Lesser Black-backed Gull *(Larus fuscus)* and the Great Black-backed Gull *(Larus marinus)*.

The picture above shows two young Great Black-backed Gulls, which are 'natives' of Surtsey, standing on the edge of the lava cliff where their parents had their nest, and on the right there is another young of the same species among the boulders on a Surtsey beach.

Besides the 13 species of sea-birds from the neighbouring islands regularly visiting Surtsey, a great number of migratory birds are observed every year on or around Surtsey. Migratory birds from the mainland of Iceland often fly over Surtsey in the autumn on their way towards the British Isles, where they winter or proceed further south.

In the spring migratory birds often land on Surtsey to take a rest after the long flight over the ocean on their way to Iceland and Greenland.

Colonisation of plants on Surtsey

The formation of the island of Surtsey by the submarine eruption which began in November 1963 off Iceland´s south coast is a unique geological event. Since the eruption came to an end in June 1967, the surface and shape of Surtsey have undergone a rapid transformation by the action of the heat and moisture in the volcanic material and by the ocean waves, current and wind in a much shorter time than was expected, as indicated above.

The development of Surtsey has been of great interest world–wide. Scientist from other countries came to follow the eruption and, later on, the development of this rare island in cooperation with Icelandic scientists.

To prevent pollution by man, human access to Surtsey is restricted. One of the most fascinating facets of the post-eruption studies has been the way in which plants have been carried by natural means to the island and colonized this bare and sterile land that rose from the sea in such a sudden and dramatic fashion.

From the beginning attempts were made to register how living organisms were carried to Surtsey. The shore was surveyed to record plants which had arrived by the sea. The arrival of seeds and spores, carried by wind and birds was also carefully observed. In the beginning individual plants which were found to be growing on the island were marked on the spot and on a map. Later on as the plant species grew in numbers an estimation of plants pr.unit of area had to be applied.

It was first noted, that coastal plants had begun to grow near the Surtsey shore, most likely developing from seeds brought in by the ocean, possibly also by clumps of turf, sea-weed, driftwood or other debris washed ashore from nearby islands. Birds have also transported seeds to the island, and by 1991 a total number of around 25 species of higher plants have been registered. Some of them have achieved considerable growth, while others have not been able to survive. Therefore only about eighteen higher plant species are currently growing on Surtsey, one fourth of which being only single specimens.

The most common higher plant on Surtsey is the Sea-beach Sandwort or Sea-purslane *(Honckenya peploides)*, a perennial plant, which has spread extensively in the sandy areas. The Sea-beech Sandwort can be seen in the picture bottom right (p. 173), and in the foreground of the picture bottom left (p. 172).

172

Another widely distributed higher plant which also arrived early on Surtsey is Lyme-grass or Dune-grass *(Elymus arenarius)*. It often grows in sandy areas together with the Sandwort, as can be seen in the picture below on the left, where Lyme grass can be spotted in the background.

The third plant now growing in the Surtsey sand is the Sea Lungwort *(Mertensia maritima)*. These three species constitute a plant association, the first permanent coastal vegetation on the island of Surtsey.

The picture on the right shows the first Daisy or Mayweed (*Tripleurospermum maritimum* or *Matricaria maritima*) to grow on Surtsey. It was found in the main crater, Surtur II.

On the surface of the lava, both inside the old craters and on the flat lava area, the Arctic-Alpine moss *(Rhacomitrium lanuginosum)* is spreading (see the picture of the inside of the crater, Surtur II, on p.172, top left). Arctic or Alpine Pearlwort *(Sagina saginodes)* together with Sea Alkali-grass or Sea Spear-grass *(Puccinellia maritima)* and Annual Meadow-grass *(Poa annua)* also grow on the flat lava. Between them these three plants are beginning to cover the sandy parts of the lava area with vegetation.

As the years go by the vegatation spreads, although so far less than 2% of the island has any plant coverage. The conditions for plants on Surtsey are very harsh. In spite of high rainfall, there is lack of water as it seeps quickly through the porous sand and lava surface except for the small amounts which are retained in tiny puddles in the lava. The sand is also still low in nutritional content, except in some areas, where droppings from sea-birds provide plants with nitrogen. Most of the island is exposed to frequent salt spray. It will, therefore, take vegetation a long time to get sufficiently established to cover an appreciable part of Surtsey.

The birds have had, and will have, considerable influence on the development of vegetation on Surtsey. Birds have transported seeds and plants to the island. Their droppings and fish waste from the food they carry to their nesting sites have boosted the fertility of the soil. In turn, the birds also benefit from the advancing vegetation as it provides shelter for their nests and protection for their young.

173

fire in Hekla 1970

An eruption started in Mt Hekla about 9.30 p.m. on May 5 1970. The last major eruption of Hekla took place in 1947-48. Shorter intervals between Hekla eruptions have occurred, but this eruption took scientists and laymen alike entirely unawares. It was not until 20.48 that same night that earth tremors were registered on seismographs in Reykjavik, the biggest tremor occurring at 21.40. As soon as the eruption started a black column of smoke rose from the mountain and in neighbouring districts red flames of fire were seen to reach a long way up the eruption column, which reached a height of almost 15 km. The wind was blowing from the south-east when the eruption began, directing the ashes in a north-westerly direction. Near the Burfell power station lumps of pumice as big as a man's fist rained down together with the ashes. As usual, the tephra-fall was most intense during the first few hours, the tephra layer being up to 17 cm. thick in the centre of the tephra-fall area. To judge by the fire columns that were seen it soon became clear that the Hekla ridge had not opened lengthwise as happens when there are major eruptions in the volcano proper. Instead volcanic fissures had opened in three separate places. Two of them were in the upper parts of the mountain slopes, one on the north side, marked 1 on the map below, and the other, marked 2 on the map, on the south side. The third fissure, which opened at the same time as the other two, was not in Hekla proper, but to the north-east of the mountain near the old craters in Skjólkvíar (3). At the beginning the eruption from the fissure in the south-side of Hekla was by far the most

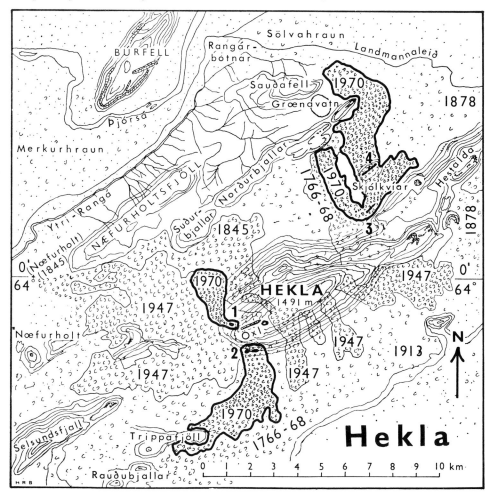

Hekla

The map shows Hekla and its immediate vicinity. The three volcanic areas which became active on May 5 1970 are marked 1, 2, and 3. Area 1 to the north of Hekla's Shoulder Crater produced the least lava, the eruption there lasting only a short period. Much more lava flowed from the crater row on the south side of Hekla (2), reaching as far as Trippafjöll. The Skjólkvíar eruption to the north-west of Hekla proper (3) was of the longest duration. The resulting lava inundated the Hringlandahraun lava of 1766-68. New active craters opened up in a sand hill in the Skjólkvíar area on May 20, from which lava flowed all the way past Sauðafell above Rangárbotnar.

A few older lava areas are indicated on the map, e.g. Næfurholtshraun of 1845, when the farm Næfurholt was moved because of the lava flow.

The photograph on the right is of the Skjólkvíar eruption (3 on the map) in the evening of May 7 1970. The eruption moved erratically from one place to another along the volcanic fissure. A small fire hole which opened in a closed part of the fissure sometimes developed into the most active vent within half an hour. Red-hot lava splashes were hurled hundreds of metres up in the air and then fell back, still glowing, on the crater rims where they flattened out and solidified.

An eruption in the second lot of Skjólkvíar craters (picture left and marked 4 on the map on p.174) in the evening of May 24 1970. A view from Norðurbjallar over the new lava flows and the crater rows in the Skjólkvíar sand hill. The north-east side of Hekla is in the background.

The advance of the lava edge in Skjólkvíar (right) was accompanied by some grinding noise and clatter as the insulating hardened crust on top of the red-hot lava flow pressed forward and disintegrated. Where the lava advanced at its highest speed, the molten basalt lava was easily visible. Many a fascinated spectator watched in awe the advancing lava stream which in a few days inundated twenty km^2 of land, sand, old lava and grassland alike.

The lava edge to the north-east of Norðurbjallar (right) in the late evening of May 24 1970. Motor vehicles could be driven right up to the edge of the lava, but their drivers had to take care not to leave them too close to the lava since its advance was more rapid than many realized. In one night the motor car tracks seen in the picture were engulfed by the firy lava.

forceful, the lava masses being ejected to a height of approximately 750 m from a row of craters. From it a continuous red-hot lava stream of more or less uniform width flowed down the slopes of Hekla in the direction of Trippafjöll.

The eruption in, and the lava flow from, the fissure in the north side of Hekla was less intense than in the other areas, whereas the Skjólkvíar eruption soon increased in intensity. There the lava flow engulfed a snow-covered area, melting the snow as it advanced. Ice and fire were in a very real contact here, causing dark-brown streams of water to rush down newly-formed river beds. In the first four days of the eruption the new lava spread over an area of about 19 km^2.

As the eruption started at the beginning of the lambing season and all vegetation was just entering a sensitive revival period after the winter, some livestock were killed by fluor poisoning in the areas that were worst hit by the tephra fall both in the South and North of Iceland, even though in many places sheep and cattle were kept inside under medical attention or transferred to unpolluted areas.

An analysis of the eruption material revealed the same chemical structure as that of the lava produced in the 1947-48 eruption of Hekla (andesite). The crater, marked 1 on the map on page 174, on the north side of the Hekla ridge erupted for only a short time, being the highest area that was active during this eruption. There the lava-flow had completely ceased by the evening of May 6. The eruption in the south side of the mountain (2) continued a little longer where a large volume of lava flowed all the way to the Trippafjöll, covering an old lava dating from the 1766-68 eruption. In this area no lava was seen to flow after May 9, but there was red-hot lava in the crater and a lot of smoke much longer.

Of the three volcanic areas which became active on May 5 the third (marked 3 on the map) erupted longest, being on the lowest level. It was fascinating to watch the fire columns constantly shifting from one end of the fissure to the other. Heavy thuds and rumbling noise accompanied the explosions which ejected the red-hot lava masses as high as 500 m up in the air. Later crater cones were built up by the solidified ejecta, confining the eruption to a few vents that were at first all active simultaneously. By May 12, however, only one of the vents remained active. The lava from these vents flowed mainly in two directions, i.e. across the Hringlanda lava of 1766-68 in the direction of Norðurbjallar and downwards by the Hestalda mountain ridge. The lava surrounded a big sand hill in Skjólkvíar.

An overnight stay near the Skjólkvíar craters (marked 4 on the map on p. 174) was an unforgettable experience. Many of the sand hill craters were active simultaneously, presenting a veritable 'candlestick of craters'. This area was easily accessible by motorized transport. Hence, there was a ceaseless flow of tourists to these craters. To the right in the picture there is a lava rivulet issuing from the vents.

In the afternoon of May 20 the lava ceased to flow from the last active vent in this area, but about the same time a new volcanic fissure, lying in the direction NE to SW, opened up about one kilometre further to the north, i.e. on the north side of the sand hill mentioned above. In the beginning there were about 20 eruption columns in a fissure that was about one km long, but they soon decreased in number. A voluminous stream of lava flowed from this volcanic area (marked 4 on the map on page 174). The lava flowed in a northerly direction past the end of Sauðafell. Motor cars could be driven right up to the craters and the edge of the lava, so hardly ever has an active volcanic area in Iceland been more easily accessible than this one.

The lava flowing down the crater walls travelled at a speed of 3-5 m a second and the edge of the lava 4 km away from the crater sometimes advanced 5-10 metres an hour. Some vegetation was engulfed by the lava and a few hours old motor car tracks disappeared for ever under the advancing lava wall.

In front of it there were silent spectators, retreating as they watched in awe these stupendous convulsions of the land which 11 centuries ago received the name of Iceland but which might just as well have been called **'Fireland'**.

Hekla eruption 1980-81

Only 10 years after the 1970 eruption of Hekla, it woke up again quite unexpectedly in a new eruption at 13:27 on August 17 1980. This was then the shortest period between Hekla eruptions on record. The ridge of the mountain split open and a great deal of lava poured forth. This eruption, however, lasted only a few days.

Then there was another short eruption in Hekla, which started in the morning of April 9 1981. This time the lava flowed from the top crater, mainly on either side of Litla Hekla. These lava flows, as well as older ones, are shown on the map to the right.

This second short eruption was over on April 16 1981 and was considered a continuation of the August 1980 eruption rather than a separate Hekla eruption.

When there are eruptions from the top or 'shoulder' of the Hekla ridge, the mountain's shape often undergoes a change, sometimes resulting in a slightly increased hight, as was the case of the 1947 and 1980-81 eruptions.

The picture below is a view from a spot above Selsund Farm toward the eruption in the shoulder of the Hekla ridge at night on August 17 1980.

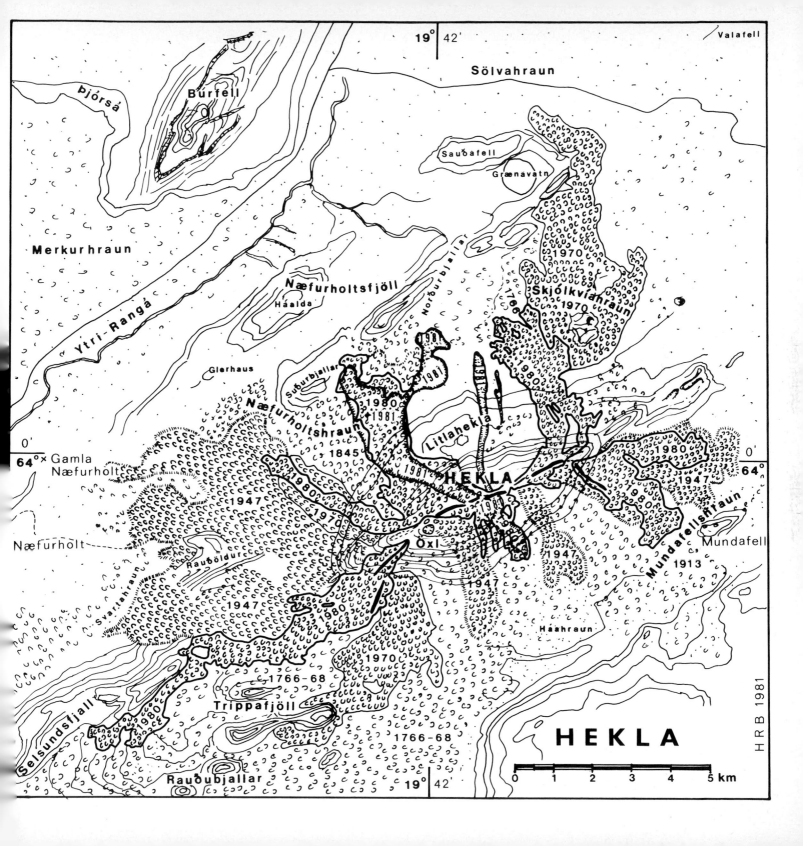

HEKLA

The picture above is a view towards Hekla from one of the many lava flows from this most famous Icelandic volcano. It was taken on August 17 1980, the first day of that completely unexpected eruption. Hardly any measurable tremors or earthquakes were detected on seismographs prior to its inception.

An outline of the history of Mt. Hekla was given on p.123 above, and the map on p. 120 of the areas of volcanic activity in Iceland indicates the years of volcanic eruptions in Hekla. The map on p. 181 shows many of the lava flows produced by Hekla. But as these lava flows have overrun older ones, layer upon layer, later lava flows have often completely or partly hidden their immediate and even distant forerunners, including some old volcanic sites in the vicinity of Hekla. Therefore only the newest lava flows can be shown on one map. The Næfurholt-lava of 1845 is the result of a major eruption. The farm had to be removed from its old site (*Gamla Næfurholt*) to a new site (*Næfurholt*).

This picture (right) was taken on the first night of the 1980 Hekla eruption. It is a view from a hill above Selsund Farm towards the eruption in the shoulder of the Hekla ridge. The crater row lights up the eruption cloud above the mountain, adding a red tinge to the dark-blue sky over the area.

182

A short Hekla eruption started in the morning of April 9 1981. Some tremors had been registered on seismographs between 22:00 and 23:00 on April 8, becoming more intense between 2 and 5 in the morning on April 9, when the eruption began. The picture on the left is a day-time view towards Hekla on April 10 1981. The smoke with ash from the eruption covers the top ridge of the mountain where the crater rift opened. Note the smoke ring above the eruption column, looking like a playful whiff produced by a giant cigarette smoker.

The picture below on the left is a view towards the highest peak of the Hekla ridge, as seen from Rauðakambur, the eastern part of the ridge itself, on May 17 1981, when that year's eruption had come to an end. The top crater of Hekla is still generating smoke, and so does the hot ash covering the ridge in the foreground.

Below is a view towards the Hekla ridge as seen from the highland-road on the way to Landmannalaugar. The picture was taken on September 27 1982, about one and a half years after the 1981 eruption. Except for the top crater itself, Hekla had again donned a cover of snow.

The picture on page 185 is a view of the lava flow from the top crater of Hekla on April 10 1981. The lava flows down the steep sides of the mountain, falling into two separate streams on either side of the hillside ridge called Litla Hekla. The picture was taken between hailstorms at night from the hill Glerhaus near the foothills of Hekla.

The picture on pp. 186-187 shows a windswept column of smoke and ash from the April 1981 Hekla eruption. It illustrates how volcanic ashes are dispersed over large areas by the wind. The thickest layers of ash are found nearest to the eruption site underneath the centre of the windswept column.

Grímsvötn eruption 1983

Grímsvötn is an active volcanic area below the ice cover of the Vatnajökull glacier (see pp. 58-61). Normally Grímsvötn is in the form of a depression in the ice sheet west of the central part of the glacier. Even between phases of volcanism part of the ice cover is melted by subterranean heat. Thus Grímsvötn is an ice-dammed lake, but very little or no water is visible as it is covered by enormous masses of floating ice. At intervals the Grímsvötn basin is discharged of its water by violent glacier bursts through channels underneath the glacier.

Because of its remote location in the middle of the glacier, Grímsvötn is believed to have erupted more often than records indicate. Minor eruptions underneath the ice cover may also have occurred without breaking through to the surface of the ice.

Early in the morning of May 29 1983 seismographs near Vatnajökull showed tremors, that might indicate volcanic eruption somewhere in the glacier.

At 10:35 a.m. the pilots of an airoplane flying over the Grímsvötn, reported that an eruption had started there. The picture above was taken from an airoplane on May 30 1983. The glacier is mostly covered by clouds, but the eruption column has by now reached a height of about 8 km above the surface of the glacier.

The picture on the right was taken on May 1983 from an airoplane flying below the clouds over Grímsvötn. The eruption had melted a hole, of about 300 m in diameter, in the ice cover of the Grímsvötn lake, the water surface in the hole being covered with slush and ice floes. There were ash explosions in the middle of the open water, apparently in a crater just below the water surface. A narrow strip of ash had spread a distance of about 5 km to the south over the glacier.

After June 2 there were no signs of an active eruption. On June 5 the open water was free of ice. Now, however, there was a small island in the middle of the lake.

The eruption which began at 1:55 a.m. on January 23 1973 on Heimaey, the biggest island in the Vestmannaeyjar archipelago, and very close to the only town on the island, came without any warning whatsoever so it took everyone by a complete surprise. True, vague earth tremors had been felt on Heimaey from 22:00 onwards in the previous evening , but there were no sharp tremors until 1:40 a.m. just before the eruption began. Then the earth opened just 200 m from Kirkjubær, the easternmost part of the town on Heimaey.

Eye-witnesses said the first volcanic activity, which was spotted in a small field, looked like fire in dry grass.

The earth´s crust then split open in a rift that lay in both directions from this spot. Soon the resulting eruption fissure had reached a length of 1600 m , stretching from the end of the landing air strip in the middle of the higher part of the island in a northterly direction through the field seen in the picture above, through Urðir on the coast, and out into the sea in the direction of the harbour entrance near Ystiklettur. In the above picture the islands of Elliðaey and Bjarnarey, as well as the south coast of the mainland, are seen in the background.

Never before in Iceland's history had an eruption begun so close to an urban settlement as in this instance.

190

Heimaey eruption 1973

The Heimaey eruption 1973 came as a complete surprise to everyone. The volcano Helgafell on the island of Heimaey is about 5000 years old, and was considered to be extinct. The two pictures (above left and above), taken on the same spot on the slopes of the Helgafell cone, are both views of the same area. The picture on the left, a view over the Kirkjubær home field in the easternmost part of Heimaey, was taken before the 1973 eruption, whereas the picture above was taken in the morning of the first day of the eruption.

Here the fields have become black with volcanic ash, and there is a fissure that extends into the sea. Elliðaey can be seen in the background of both pictures, whereas in the picture above Bjarnarey is hidden behind the eruption smoke. The morning sun is shining on the upper part of the eruption column, but the crater row is in the shade. The crater rim in the middle of the fissure is moving to the side under the pressure of the glowing molten lava in the crater bowl.

191

Above on the left is a view from the slopes of the volcanic cone of Helgafell in the early morning of the first day of the Heimaey eruption, January 23 1973. Note the short distance, only 200 m, between the houses and the volcanic fissure. All the houses seen in this picture were later engulfed by the advancing lava, which is now 100 m thick above these houses.

The picture above on the right is a view from the houses of Kirkjubær towards the fire row before dawn on the first day of the eruption. This is the view that met many of the inhabitants of Vestmannaeyjar when they woke up early in the morning that fateful day of January 1973.

On p. 193 (right), there is a general view along the crater row from the old volcano Helgafell. This picture was also taken in the morning of the first day of the eruption.

The picture below on left was also taken before dawn in the morning of January 23 1973, shortly after the eruption began. It is a view towards the crater row on the fissure, as seen from the Skansinn, near the former coastline of Heimaey.

The picture below on the right shows part of the crater row on the fissure. The explosions in the craters sent fiery lumps of lava in different directions high into the air.

From the beginning of the Heimaey eruption in the early morning of January 23 1973, the volcanic fissure was very active. It soon became one constantly erupting row of lava columns, extending the whole length of the 1600 m long fissure, - one solid wall of fire. A close look revealed a very interesting pattern of single lava vents in the row (see the picture on the left). The red hot molten lava was hurled high up in the air, partly falling back into the crater bowl, but also often swaying to the sides and building up high walls, crater rims, on both sides of the fissure. But the sides of a volcanic crater were not always strong enough to withstand the heavy pressure from the lava lake inside the crater. Therefore the sides were moving apart, giving more space for the molten lava inside the crater. The production of lava was considerable so soon it began to flow downhill in a stream that found its way down to the sea.

But what happened to the townspeople of Vestmannaeyjar at this critical juncture? The residents of the eastern part of the town woke up to the roar of the eruption and reacted quickly, when they realized what was happening. They got dressed and informed the police and their nearest neighbours. By good luck the entire local fishing fleet was in port because of a storm the day before. The people went down to the harbour and most were taken from there by fishing vessels to Þorlákshöfn on the mainland. From there they were bussed to Reykjavik. About 300 went to Reykjavík by air. The evacuation of 5000 people went very smoothly. It was almost complete by the morning of the first day of the eruption. The only people left on Heimaey were 2-300 key personnel engaged in essential services. The weather was good in the morning of the first day of the eruption, but the sea was rough, and many became seasick during the crossing over to the mainland.

During the eruption ships sailed to and from Vestmannaeyjar harbour. Clouds from the lava flowing into the sea mixed with ash from the eruption reduced the visibility when ships were entering the harbour (picture above right).
As usual for a fissure eruption, the crater row soon developed into a single active crater. The picture on the right is a view from the Helgafell towards the crater on February 2 1973.

The picture above was taken in the middle of February 1973 after a snowfall. The rock Heimaklettur is in the background. On the right there is a wall of tephra that had been piled up by bulldozers in the hope that it could prevent the lava flow gobbling up more houses. This wall did not prove to be a sufficient protection. Later on a great lava stream pushed the wall forward, burying almost all the houses seen in this picture.

As mentioned above the crater row had developed into a single volcanic crater in February when the picture below was taken. The houses in the foreground were in the eastern part of the town and were later inundated by a lava flow.

The eruption varied a great deal in intensity. During its most violent phases glowing chunks of lava flew far into the town. Some houses caught fire if these 'bombs' shot in through the windows. Many house owners therefore, closed the windows of their houses from the outside with steel plates. Above is a picture of a stately old house on fire on January 28 1973 while the angry crater spews fire and brimstone in the background.

Glowing chunks of lava were flying high up into the air and raining down on the site where the picture was taken. When fist-sized stones landed on one´s helmet, they split open baring the red hot lava inside although the stone had become black on the outside during its long flight in the air.

The picture on the right (p. 197) shows the crater in action during the night of February 19 1973.

The Vestmannaeyjar harbour is naturally of priceless value to a community that depends for its livelihood on fishing and fish processing. Therefore every possible effort was made to prevent the harbour from damage or destruction by the lavaflow. One of the most important measures taken was to pump enormous quantities of seawater onto one side of the lava flow in an attempt to change its course and slow it down. This first attempt was made near the harbour entrance when the pumping machinery of a sand dredger was used for the purpose.

The picture on the left is a view from the harbour entrance towards the lava flow, which stopped there. On March 3 1973 it was still glowing at night. The erupting crater can be seen in the background.

The picture below on the left is a view from the harbour on April 7. Fishing vessels are landing capelin, the processing of which is underway in the fish meal plants, generating wealth even though the volcano is spreading fire and brimstone over the town. The eruption has now built up a volcanic cone, which was given the name Eldfell, near the centre of the fissure. On the right below there is a view from the new lava towards the rock Heimaklettur on March 4 1973. The lava flow stopped before it reached Heimaklettur. If it had, it would have blocked the harbour entrance. The entrance is even much more sheltered now than before the eruption.

On the right (p. 199) is a close-up view into the crater at night on March 4 1973.

Quite early during the Heimaey eruption, attempts were made to protect the town by making barriers of slag from the eruption and using fire hoses and fire pumps to pump seawater on the advancing lava, in order to cool it down and slow down its progress. This method had been tested to some extent in a small scale experiment on Surtsey (see p. 155). On Heimaey this cooling of the lava had some effect, but the first attempt showed that the volume of water was too small and the range of the fire pumps was too short for any measure of success. More suction and lifting power was needed. When the lava flow approached the harbour breakwater at the end of February, a sand dredger was put in action on March 1. It was used to pump sea-water onto the lava, which in fact did not advance further at that spot. At the end of March, 43 pumps, obtained from the USA were mounted. Their capacity was 800-1000 l/sec, and their lifting height capacity 100 m through 1000 m long pipes. This equipment made it possible to apply the dampening down effort to a much larger area of the advancing lava. During the eruption, a total of 6.2 million tons of sea-water was pumped onto the lava to cool it down. Drillings showed that the cooling had had a significant effect on the solidification of the lava and therefore slowing down its advance. The seawater pumped onto the lava contained about 220 thousand tons of salt. -The aerial photo (left) was taken over Heimaey on April 7. Lava had by then buried the easternmost part of the town. Picture above: Piping amidst lava and steam clouds rising from the cooling process.- Pictures on the right (top and bottom): A lava lake and a lava stream in May 1973.

In the evening of March 22 a 300 m wide tongue of molten lava advanced almost 150 m into the Vestmannaeyjar town. During the next few days until April 4, about 200 houses were engulfed by lava. On its way, the lava broke down sturdily constructed concrete houses and set wooden houses on fire. Sometimes the lavaflow lifted houses in its path off their foundations, pushing them forward as shown in the picture above on the left. The wooden house left of centre is about to be set on fire by the heat of the lava front. The picture above shows the same house on fire.

The photo on the left shows how the lava stopped and piled up against the fish factory building of Fiskiðjan on Strandvegur near the harbour, demolishing part of this strong concrete building. This lava was later cleared from Strandvegur and the house repaired.

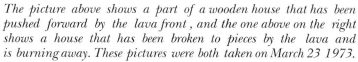

The picture above shows a part of a wooden house that has been pushed forward by the lava front, and the one above on the right shows a house that has been broken to pieces by the lava and is burning away. These pictures were both taken on March 23 1973.

The picture on the right also shows a part of a house that has been pushed forward by the lava. This scene was left unchanged for some time after the eruption came to an end to demonstrate to visitors the flimsy nature of man-made objects versus the violent forces of nature. This picture was taken on January 9 1974.

The town was never completely without electricity during the course of the eruption. The submarine cable which brought electricity from the mainland was severed by a submarine eruption off Ystiklettur on February 6 1973, but a 4000 kw diesel power station in the town generated electricity until it was engulfed by lava on March 25. After that a small generator in the fish meal factory near the western harbour took over. The large water pipeline from the mainland was severed at the same time as the electrical submarine cable, but a smaller water pipeline held and continued to supply water to Heimaey.

203

Already before the eruption came to an end work began on excavating the town and clearing away ash and debris. Thich lava could not be tackled, however. Big bulldozers and havy excavation machinery were used. The ash was transported to places on the island where the material could be used for road building and for an extension of the air strip of the Heimaey airfield.

The pictures above illustrate the enormous amount of ash which had to be removed. Many of the houses were completely buried in volcanic ash. In some cases only the top of the chimney indicated that there was a house underneath.

In the western part of the town the ash was not as thich as closer to the volcano (picture left). Even here, however, excavation machinery had to be used to clear away as much as possible of the ash before the final cleaning by hand took over.

All the houses in the foreground of the above picture were completely submerged by ash. When walking on top of the ash heaps, people found the chimneys of some of the houses convenient seats if they wanted a momentary rest. When the picture was taken on May 9 1974, considerable amounts of the ash had been removed.

The roofs of some of the houses had collapsed under the heavy weight of ash heaps. A case in point can be seen in the foreground of the picture above. The same house can be seen in the picture that was taken on August 6 1978 (above right). Then the ash had been removed down to the street level in front of the house. However, the edge of the lava flow is still too close for comfort.

This is one of the many houses whose windows were covered up with corrugated iron plates to prevent fiery chunks of lava from flying in and setting the house on fire.

The picture on the right shows an entire family clearing ash from the garden of their house.

205

This statue of an angel stands on a grave in the Vestmannaeyjar cemetary. Ash came up to the figure´s knees before the clean-up work began. The picture on the right, which was taken at the end of the clean-up work in the cemetery, indicates how thick the layer of ash was at this spot. The angel stands on the grave of Theodora Þ. Jónsdóttir, Garður of Vestmannaeyjar, who died at the age of 22 (b. December 26 1906, d. May 16 1928). Landakirkja Church is in the background.

Above is a peaceful late summer night view from the rock Ystiklettur to the town of Vestmannaeyjar on August 27 1982. Years have passed since the fateful early morning of January 23 1973, when the volcanic fissure opened and the Heimaey eruption started.

The picture on the left is a view over the new lava with the rocks Heimaklettur and Ystiklettur in the background. It was taken from the slopes of Eldfell, the new volcano from 1973, just above the memorial stone to the Reverend Jón Þorsteinsson 'the Martyr', who was killed by pirates on July 17 1627. This stone used to be at Kirkjubær, and when the lava flow approached, the stone was removed. It was subsequently placed on a new base in the Eldfell lava, right above the the spot where it stood before. Its level, however, is now about 100 m higher than before, which is the thickness of the lava above Kirkjubær.

The pictures on the right show the entrance to the harbour of Vestmannaeyjar after the eruption. It is much more sheltered now as the new lava is quite close to the Heimaklettur and Ystiklettur. The ferry Herjólfur is leaving the harbour on its way to the mainland.

210

HEIMAEY
before the eruption

Dalsfjall
Klif
Ystiklettur
Heimaklettur
Klettsnef
Kirkjubær
Urðir
Helgafell
226 m
Flugnatangi
Stakkar
Kópavík
Stórhöfði

HEIMAEY
before the eruption

0   1   2 km

HEIMAEY
before the eruption

The vertical aerial photograph on the left was taken by Landmælingar Íslands (Icelandic Survey Department) about 12 years before the Heimaey eruption started on January 23 1973.

Some place names have been marked on the photograph. It shows quite clearly how exposed the entrance of the harbour used to be before the lava flow from the eruption filled up a considerable sea area near the rocks of Heimaklettur and Ystiklettur.

Before the eruption there was only one landing strip for Vestmannaeyjar Airport. One of the reasons was a lack of suitable filling material on Heimaey for road and airfield construction. A limited amount of material had been taken from the lower slopes of the old volcanic cone of Helgafell, every effort being made not to damage its beautiful shape. This quarry shows up in the aerial photograph.

On the other hand the eruption produced ample material for these purposes. The lighthouse at Urðir was engulfed by the lava flow shortly after the rift opened up in the fields near by it as marked with a broken line in the photograph.

The main Vestmannaeyjar lighthouse and an important weather station are located at Stórhöfði on Heimaey.

HEIMAEY
after the eruption

The vertical aerial photograph on the right was taken by Landmælingar Íslands (Icelandic Survey Department) after the Heimaey eruption had come to an end.

The photograph has had the same place names inserted as the one on p.212. Besides, the new Eldfell has been added. A line through the row of craters towards the airfield and through the Eldfell volcano shows the direction of the fissure which opened on January 23 1973, when the eruption started. This photograph is showing very clearly how much more sheltered the harbour entrance is after the eruption. There is a long fjord between the new lava and the rocks Ystiklettur and Heimaklettur, in front of the entrance at the old breakwaters. By comparing the two photographs it is also clear how great a part of the town has been engulfed by the lava, and also the addition to the area of Heimaey. A new western part of the town has been built, and the airfield has got 2 landing airstrips. Even the hole in the Helgafell has been repaired with ash.- The Heimaey-eruption was certainly a great loss, but there were also some gains.

On the following page (page 214) there is a view over the Vestmannaeyjar town from the Klif, after the eruption. In the foreground is the harbour, then the town. Beside the old Helgafell, a new neighbour has risen, the volcano Eldfell, lava from which has engulfed the eastern part of the town. Normal life and activity is back in full swing.

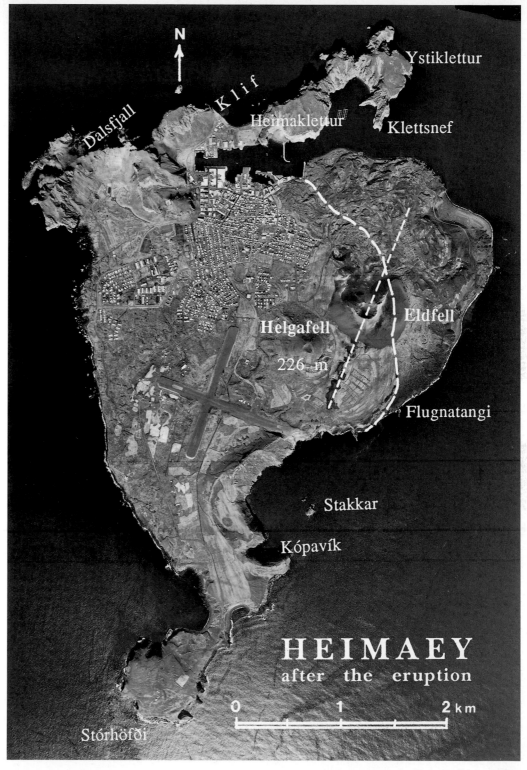

HEIMAEY
after the eruption

0   1   2 km

Krafla eruption 1975-84

The Krafla eruption 1975 began in the morning of December 20 near Leirhnjúkur in the Krafla caldera, near Mývatn. This place is a well known volcanic area, a part of the active volcanic zone of Iceland, as is shown on the map on page 120. This long lasting Krafla eruption from 1975 to 1984, with some shorter or longer intervals between single eruptions, is very similar to the so called Mývatn-fires which took place in the same area 1724-1746, also with several single eruptions and shorter or longer intervals between. The Mývatn period of eruptions started with a great explosive eruption on the slopes of the mountain Krafla. Then a big explosive crater, Víti, was formed. Picture above shows Víti, as it looks today, with the mountain Krafla in the background.

As mentioned above, steam vents and mud pots sometimes emerge in volcanic craters when an eruption has come to an end. They may also be forerunners of eruptions, appearing on the spot where an eruption will subsequently start. The photo above left was taken at Leirhnjúkur in the Krafla caldera where a large steam vent and fumarole of this type (called Nína) cropped up in an explosion on a hill on August 2 1977. Soon afterwards (on September 8 1977) the third Krafla eruption began in a fissure north of Leirhnjúkur.

The picture at the bottom left is of a recently solidified ropy lava stream from that eruption, 3 km north of Leirhnjúkur.

The picture above shows rifts in the process of opening on the surface of the Krafla caldera. When originally positioned there, the pipe ends joined in the middle. Now there is a considerable gap.

Below we see a rift that has opened so that pipes running across its direction had to be extended. The diatomaceous earth factory in Bjarnarflag near Lake Mývatn is in the background.

The fifth Krafla eruption began on July 10 1980 in the Snagaborgir craters in Gjástykki. By July 18 it was all over. The lava field from this eruption covered an area of about 5-6 km². It was called Snaga-hraun, because it encircled a hill by the name of Snagi. Above is a picture of sunrise over Gjástykki at that time, viewed through a cloud of smoke from the erupting Snagaborgir.

On the left above is an aerial view of the lava river issuing from the Snagaborgir craters during the eruption of July 1980. The crater row is on the far left in the picture. The lava flows in a northerly direction along Gjástykki. Large pieces of solidified lava float on the surface of the lava stream like chunks of ice on a river.

The picture at the bottom left was also taken from the air, showing the same lava stream farther north. Here the lava moves more slowly, spreading over a larger area.

Above is a view from the hill Snagi of the lava stream flowing over Gjástykki in a northerly direction.

Below we see lava engulfing a vegetational cover in the Gjástykki area.

The picture on the right (p.221) is a view from the hill Snagi to the Snagaborgir craters during the eruption of July 1980.

On pp.222-223 there is a view of the glowing lava fountain, rising like a continuous wall of fire, at the beginning of the seventh Krafla eruption at Éthólaborgir about 3 p.m. on January 30, 1981, - quite a magnificent spectacle.

After the eight Krafla eruption in November 1981 had come to an end the earth´s surface near the Leirhnjúkur began to swell, as it had done before after the end of each eruption. In early 1982 measurements indicated, that the pressure in the magma cambers had reached a maximum level. The rise of the earth´s surface had slowed down, which was the usual sign of a decrease in the afflux of magma from below. Then there was a period of very little or no surface swelling, broken by periods of a slow rise. In August 1982 there was an increase in earth tremors with a simultaneous slight land rise. This activity diminished again in September. This was the first sign of that the earth´s crust above the magma chamber was about to split open.

Similar land rise and earthquake periods occurred in October -December 1982, then in June and September-October 1983, again in February and in August 1984. These were all signs that volcanic activity in the Krafla caldera had not come to an end, the course and timing of subsequent events was quite uncertain. It was evident, however, that the pressure in the main magma chamber was sufficient to force open a passage up to the surface so that only a minor development one way or the other might trigger off an eruption.

At 20:25 on September 4 1984 sinking of the land surface started in the Krafla caldera. Shortly afterwards local seismographs registered some earth tremors. The earthquakes persisted, and at 23:49 the first glow from erupting lava was spotted. The first fissure to appear was 2 km long, but an hour later the total length of the

numerous separate eruption fissures was more than 8 km, most of them in similar places as earlier fissures in the Krafla caldera. Large amounts of lava flowed from the rifts during the first few hours of the eruption, but soon the lava flow diminished with part of the fissures closing.

By September 7 the lava eruption near Leirhnjúkur had come to an end, leaving a big steam vent which ejected mud and ash.

In the days that followed the lava eruption in the northern part of the fissure grew in intensity with lava flowing mostly in a northerly direction along the Gjástykki (see map on p. 217).

The pictures above were taken from the air on September 9, 1984.

On the left (p. 226) there is a view into the very active crater at Éthólaborgir, where a sizable cone had built up (see map on p. 217). The lava flowed northwards, spreading over a wide area, part of which had not been covered by lava from this Krafla eruptions before (see picture above). It was interesting to note the way the lava flow, like a bulldozer, pushed large amounts of sand before its advancing thrust when engulfing sandy terrain. Conversely, areas covered with vegetation were marked by gas explosions and flashing gas flames before succumbing to the advancing lava. The lava frequently followed old rifts, widening them as it surged forward. After entering and filling up one rift, the lava sometimes reappeared in another rift nearby with the deceptive look of a new eruption.

At the beginning of this chapter it was mentioned that the course of the 1975-84 Krafla eruption, was very similar to that of the 1724-1746 'Mývatn Fires', which occurred in the same area. In both cases there were several single eruptions with intervals of varying length.

During the Mývatn Fires there were many eruptions in the 6 years of 1724-1729, after which there was a lull of 17 years before the final short but fierce eruption of 1746.

In the recent Krafla eruptions the corresponding intervening periods were first the 7 years of 1975-1981, then an interval of only 2 years before the September 1984 eruption started. From that time and until the time of writing in 1991 some rising and sinking movements of the surface in the Krafla caldera continued. No one can tell what the future holds, of course.

It is well known that the Mid-Atlantic Ridge cuts through the volcanic zone of Iceland, where the edges of the plates on each side of the ridge meet. These plates, and with them the two parts of Iceland on each side of the ridge, are moving apart by about 1 cm a year. This means that during the nearly 250 years between the Mývatn and Krafla eruptions, Iceland has been widened by nearly 5 m. This movement is not even, however, as it occurs during the so-called rifting periods only. The total opening of rifts across the fissure swarm during the Krafla eruptions was not far from 4-5 m. If the Krafla events have come to an end now, there may be a similar development around the year 2225. If such events commence earlier, the opening up of the fissure swarm, would not need to be more than 2 cm for each year from the last year of the Krafla eruption, provided the plates on each side of the Atlantic Ridge continue to move at the same pace as they do now.

Above is an aerial view from the south over the Krafla caldera. In the foreground (left) is a large steam vent, ejecting a mixture of steam, mud and ash. This eruption emerged near Leirhnjúkur after the lava eruption there had come to an end on September 7. The active volcanic crater-cone at Éthólaborgir, and the northward flowing lava from there are in the background.

Below, a part of the Krafla caldera is seen from the north. The lava is flowing from the Éthólaborgir craters on September 9, 1984, over a sandy terrain, filling all hollows on its way.

The ninth eruption of the Krafla fires came finally to an end in the afternoon of September 18, 1984.

Hekla eruption 1991

An eruption started in Mt Hekla at about 17:00 on January 17 1991. Earth tremors were not registered until half an hour before rifts opened up on the mountain ridge, and lava started to flow down the slopes in three places. The eruption was first noted from two airplanes. During the evening it snowed, but in between it cleared up a bit, revealing lava fountains and a lavaflow as in the photograph above, which is an aerial view through an opening in the clouds.

229

The photograph on p.229 was taken from an aeroplane of the Icelandic Coast Guard by Captain Kristján Jónsson in the evening of January 17 1991, shortly after the eruption started. It is a view through an opening in the snowstorm clouds. A rift has opened up in the Hekla mountain ridge, and the lava fountains and the lava flow could be seen for a short moment.

The photograph left is a view from the air along the south-eastern slopes of Hekla on January 19, showing the lava flow and the then only one still active crater at the north-east end of the Hekla ridge.

The top right picture (p.231) is a side-view of Hekla late in the afternoon of January 20. The crater at the north-east end of the ridge is still erupting.

The picture bottom right (p.231) is a view from the air along the top ridge of Mt Hekla, showing the large areas covered with new lava flows (black). The rifts which opened when the eruption started on January 17 can be seen. However, the lava flow filled some of them up later on. The top crater on Hekla´s highest peak did not open up.

Seismographs registered earthquakes at 16:36 on January 17, 1991 in the Hekla area. At 17:00 continuous eruption-tremors started, and at 17:10 the eruption column was measured 11.5 km high. Thus the first eruption rifts in Hekla seem to have opened up between 17:00 and 17:10. Seismographs continued to register earthquakes, reaching a maximum intensity at 18:00. After that earthquakes diminished. This indicates that upstream of magma (and lava flow) reached its maximum at that time. It is a well known fact that volcanic eruptions are most powerful at the beginning, and minor eruptions like this one are reduced in power very quickly. Therefore, there was a considerable flow of thin lava down the slopes of the Hekla ridge at the very beginning of the eruption. As there was a snow-storm at the time when the eruption started, it was difficult to get a general view of the situation. Intermittently during the snowstorm, however, the lava-fountains and the lavaflow down the slopes could be seen from the countryside below and from the air. During the second day of the eruption the snowstorm virtually precluded a view of the volcano. By January 19 and 20, 1991 the snowstorm had died down, but then only one of the 3 or 5 rifts which opened up in the beginning was found to be still active. On the other hand the new lava flow from the eruption was easy to follow, as black areas against the white background of a snow-covered landscape. At the end of the second day of the eruption only the rift on the north-eastern slope of Hekla was still active.

The volcanic eruption which started in Hekla at about 17:00 on January 17 1991 is the 17th recorded Hekla eruption since the settlement of Iceland in 874 AD, and the 4th in this century. When the 1947 eruption started, the Hekla had not been active for 101 years. The next eruption occurred 22 years later, in 1970, lasting for 2 months. Then only 10 years later there was the very short 1980-81 eruption. Then the volcanic activity lasted, with intermittent pauses, for only 1-2 weeks. Now, in January 1991, only 10 years after the last eruption, Hekla became active again. These last three eruptions have all been rather small with an estimated lava production of less than 0.2 km³, and lasting only for short periods of time.

As mentioned above, the 1991 eruption was fairly violent in the very beginning, but as early as the second day the activity diminished considerably. Such a short duration of the initial intense activity is quite typical of Hekla eruptions as the pressure in the magma chamber falls soon after the commensement of the lava flow.

The picture above is shows a lava-stream from the crater in the fissure on the south side of the north-eastern slopes of the Hekla ridge in the afternoon of February 24 1991. Then this crater had been active for over a month, the only one that still remained. The lava flow had spread over considerable area, covering older lava (see map on p.233).

The very short time between the eruptions of 1970, 1980-81 and 1991 is very uncharacteristic of Hekla, when compared with its performance before 1974. However, no projections can be made on future Hekla eruptions on the basis of its past history. Another point to be noted about Hekla is that earth tremors commence only a very short time before a rift opens and a lava flow begins. As mentioned above, the advance earthquake warning came only 30 minutes before the 1991 eruption started.

232

The picture above is a view from the new lava flow towards the crater which was still active on February 24 1991 and which had built up in the fissure on the south side of the north-east slopes of the Hekla ridge. The lava stream shown on p.232 emerges through a tunnel in the crater wall close to where the persons are standing. The map on the right shows in red the lava flow from the January-March Hekla eruption. The area indicated of the lava is based on aerial photograps and measurements made by geologists of the National Energy Authority of Iceland *(Orkustofnun)*. The total area of the lava flow was calculated to be about 23 km^2, so that with an estimated thickness of 4 to 9 m the total volume of the new lava might be between 0.1 and 0.2 km^3, which is similar to the volume produced in the eruptions of 1970 and 1980-81 respectively. On the map the fissures which opened up at the beginning of the eruption are marked as thick red lines, serrated on one side. The crater cone (picture above) which built up in the fissure on the south side, is marked with a circle. Dates of older lava flows are shown in black, the 1991 in red.

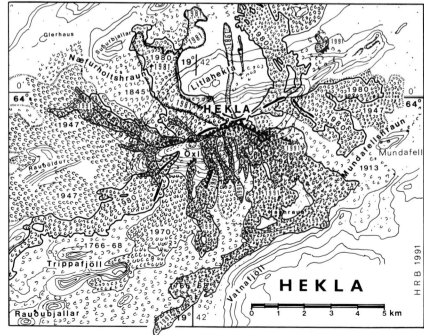

233

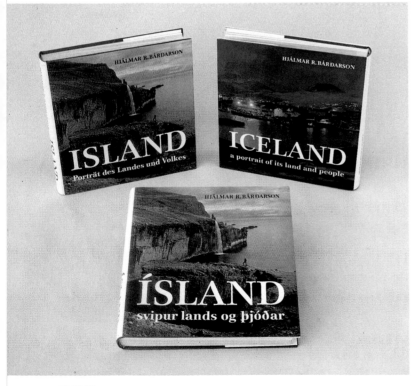

BOOKS ON ICELAND by HJÁLMAR R. BÁRÐARSON:

Ice and fire

Ice and fire is a portrait in words and pictures of the striking contrasts of Icelandic nature. Ice and fire, glaciers and volcanoes, have played an important part in the history of Iceland, and from the very first days of the settlement these two elements have often proved formidable foes. Drifting ice-floes have occasionally covered fishing grounds and blocked harbours, whilst erupting volcanoes have buried land and livestock under ash and lava. Iceland was first named after drift-ice seen along the northern shores, but such is the country´s nature that it might just as easily have been called 'Fireland' had one of its many volcanoes been active when the first viking settlers arrived. - At the beginning of the book there are descriptions and illustrations of the nature, formation, and properties of drift-ice, followed by chapters on glaciers, snow-falls and icing. The book goes on to deal with geysers, hot springs, mud-pools, caldera, solfataras, and the many kinds of volcanic eruptions. - The original editions of ice and fire have 172 pages, 205 photographs (83 in colour), and 15 explanatory maps and drawings. The new English edition (1991) has 244 pages, about 300 photographs, 180 of them in colour. This book provides a vivid, informative, and comprehensive survey of all the most interesting geological features of Iceland. *Separate Editions in English, German and Icelandic.*

ICELAND, a portrait of its land and people.

The book begins by giving an account of the first discovery of Iceland, the voyages of Irish monks, and the possibility of an Irish settlement of Iceland prior to that of the 9th century by Nordic vikings, and then goes on to describe how further viking voyages from Iceland resulted in the discovery of Greenland and America. The book traces the origins of the Icelandic nation in the intermingling of the Nordic and Celtic races and describes how this new nation formed its own unique political and social system based on chieftaincies and national assembly. The country´s subsequent history is recorded and illustrated to show how Iceland finally evolved into a modern welfare state. - Ensuing chapters present a survey of the regions of Iceland in the form of a journey around the island with stops at many historic and interesting places to reveal the way the people live in their natural surroundings. - Descriptions of Iceland´s glaciers and extensive lavafields are also included, along with an illustrated history of some of Iceland´s more recent volcanic eruptions (e.g. Hekla, Askja and Krafla). There is also a detailed record of Surtsey´s dramatic emergence from under the sea, and a day-by-day account of the famous Vestmannaeyjar eruption - and how the thriving community of Heimaey arose again from its ashes. - This attractively bound book has 428 pages, 20 chapters, and 650 photographs (220 in colour) as well as drawings and maps, providing a vivid, detailed, and lively portrait of the land and people of Iceland, both past and present. - *Separate Editions in English, German and Icelandic.*

BOOKS ON ICELAND by HJÁLMAR R. BÁRÐARSON:

BIRDS OF ICELAND. This sumptuously illustrated book has 336 pages. It gives detailed information on the distinctive features, habitats, life patterns and general behaviour of all the breeding birds of Iceland - around 70 in all - as well as some of the irregular and regular visitors. There are around 500 photographs - nearly 400 of them in colour, as well as explanatory maps and drawings. - The various species of birds are presented in groups according to their habitat, family, or behaviour: Island and Skerries, Cliff-birds, Shore-birds, Marshland-birds, Ducks, Moorland-birds, Town and Farmbirds, The Highlands, Lavafields and Woodlands, Birds of Prey, and finally Visitors and irregular breeding birds. There is a chapter on the tragic story of the last Great Auk (killed on Eldey Island off the southwest coast of Iceland in 1844) and - most important for visitors - a chapter that lists some of the most interesting places in the country for bird-watching. - Compared with the nearest European countries, there are relatively few species of breeding birds in Iceland, but their huge populations mean that the country is teeming with bird life nonetheless. The most conspicuous birds in Iceland are seabirds, ducks, and waders. Iceland has an estimated total of 13 million breeding pairs of seabirds - and naturally, seabirds are given full value in this book, along with photographs of the sea-cliffs they inhabit. The book also highlights some fascinating European rarities, like Barrow´s goldeneye, and the striking Harlequin duck. - Birds of Iceland is an absolute 'must' for anyone interested in birds in general and Icelandic birds in particular.- *Separate Editions in English, German, French, Danish and Icelandic.*

HVÍTÁ from source to sea. This book describes in word and pictures the landscape and geology of the Hvítá/Ölfusá drainage basin, but it also looks at the present and past daily life of that area, dedicating entire chapters to such historically famous places as Þingvellir and Skálholt. At the same time it offers a view of some of Iceland´s most spectacular natural phenomena, such as Gullfoss and Geysir, as well as many other lesser known and rarely sought spots that will be of interest to all travellers. - The introductory chapter takes a look at the general nature of water and the hydrologic cycle. Subsequent chapters, by following the course of a river as large as Hvítá from source to sea, thus show in detail how part of the eternal hydrologic cycle works in effect. The area of the Hvítá/Ölfusá drainage basin is 6,100 km^2, and the places that are dealt with in the book include: Kjölur and Kjalhraun between the glaciers Langjökull and Hofsjökull, the old Kjalvegur road, the geothermal area at Hveravellir, the Kerlingarfjöll group of mountains, Hvítárvatn then following Hvítá to Gullfoss. The famous Geysir also receives close attention, and so does Þingvellir, the site of Iceland´s ancient parliament. - The book contains 440 pages with 749 illustrations, drawings and maps, including 622 colour photographs. Aside from the main text, there are separate descriptions alongside the photographs. - *Separate Editions in English, German and Icelandic.*

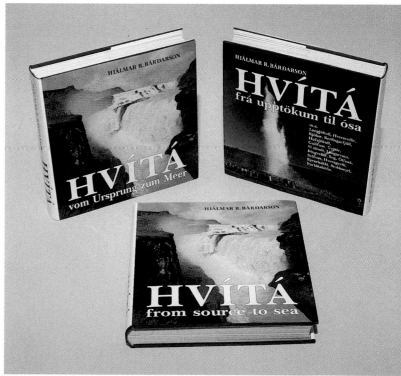

some Icelandic terms

A, Á.
á (pl. ár): river
ás: ridge
askja: caldera

B.
bakki: bank
berggangur: intrusion
bergvatnsá: mountain river
borg: lit.fortress, type of rock
    formation; city
botn: end of valley
bólstraberg: pillow lava
brekka: hill, slope
brotaberg: volcanic breccia
brún: edge, border, brow
bugða: bight, bend in a river
bunga: bulge

D.
dalbotn: end of a valley
dalmynni: mouth of a valley
dalur: valley
dalverpi: small valley
djúpberg: plutonic rock
dragá: drainage river
drangi: single rock, pinnacle
dyngja: shield volcano
dýjamosi: bogmoss

E.
eldkeila: stratovolcano
engi: meadow
ey, eyja: island
eyri: sand or gravel bank, spit

F.
farvegur: stream bed
fell: fell, hill, small mountain
fjall: mountain
fjörður: fjord
fljót: large river
flóð: flood
flói: bay, marshland
flúðir: rapids, cascades
foss: waterfall
frostmark: freezing point, zero
fönn: snow drift, snow wreath

G.
gil: ravine, gulley
gígur: crater
gjá: chasm
gljúfur: ravine, canyon
gnípa: peak, pinnacle
gos: eruption
goshver: geyser
gosmóberg: tuff, palagonite
gosmöl: tephra
grágrýti: dolerite
grettistak: erratic boulder
grjót: stones, rock
grýlukerti: icicle
gufuhver: fumarole

H.
haf: sea, ocean
haft; short strip of land
hagi: pasture land
hamar: crag
háls: hill
hávaðar: (pl) rapids
heiði: heath, moor
hellir: cave
hérað: rural district, county
hjarnmörk: firn line
hlíð: slope, mountain side
hnjúkur, hnúkur: peak
hnullungur: oval shaped stone
höfði: cape, headland
höfn: harbour
hóll: hill, hillock
hólmi: small island
hóp: land locked inlet
holt: stony hill
hraun: lava, lava field
hraundyngja: shield volcano
hreppur: county
hryggur: ridge
hvammur: grassy hollow,
hver: hot spring, geyser
hverahrúður: geyserite
hveraleir: boiling mud
hverasvæði: geothermal area
hæð: hill, height

I, Í.
ís: ice
ísaþoka: ice fog
íseyja: ice island
íshamar: ice wall
ísing: icing
ísjaðar: ice edge

J.
jaki: floe
jarðhitasvæði: geothermal
    area
jarðvegur: soil
jökulalda: moraine,
jökulá: glacial river
jökulbunga: ice cap
jökulgarður: terminal
    moraine
jökulhlaup: glacial flood
jökull: glacier
jökulskeið: ice age
jökulsker: nunatak

K.
kambur: crest, ridge
kelda: bog, well, source
kísilmyndun: silicone deposit
klappír: jutting rocks
klettur: rock, cliff face
krap: slush
kvika: magma
kvísl: tributary river

L.
laug: warm spring, bath
leir: clay, mud
leirhver: solfatara
leysingavatn: meltwater
lind: spring, well, source
lindá: spring-fed river
líparít: rhyolite
lón: lagoon,
lægð: depression
lækur: brook

M.
melur: gravel plain
móberg: palagonite, tuff
möl: gravel
mýri: swamp, marsh

N.
nes: ness, point, headland
núpur: peak

O, Ó.
oddi: tongue or point
ós: mouth of a river
óseyri: delta

R.
rennsli: flow of water
rigning: rain
rof: erosion

S.
sandur: sand
skarð: mountain pass
sker: skerry, reef
skriðjökull: outlet glacier
slétta: plain
sprengigígur: explosive crater
sprunga: crevice, fissure
stapi: table mountain
strönd: coast
stuðlaberg: basalt columns
stöðuvatn: lake
sveit: rural district

T.
tangi: point of land
tindur: peak
tjörn; pond, pool
torf: turf
tún: field, meadow

U, Ú.
undirlendi: lowland
útfall: mouth, effluent
útfelling: precipitation, deposit

V.
vað: ford
vatn: water, lake
vatnasvið: drainage basin
vík: creek
vogur: small bay, inlet
volgra: lukewarm spring
votlendi: marshland

Þ.
þing: assembly, parliament
þrepahlaup: stepflood
þröskuldur: ridge
þursaberg: palagonite, breccia

bibliography

Books and papers are arranged in alphabetical order of their authors' surnames. In the case of collective authorship the name of the work decides the order in which it is listed.

Armstrong, T., Roberts B., & Swithinbank Ch.,1966.Illustrated Glossary of Snow and Ice. Cambridge.

Árnason, Bragi, 1968. Tvívetni í grunnvatni og jöklum á Íslandi (Deuterium in Ground Water and Glaciers in Iceland). Jökull, 337-349. Reykjavík.

Áskelsson, Jóhannes, 1936. On the Last Eruption in Vatnajökull. Reykjavík.

Bárðarson (Bardarson), Guðmundur G., 1934. Islands Gletscher. Reykjavík.

Bárðarson (Bardarson), Hjálmar R., 1966. Jökulskinna, gestabók á Hrolleifsborg i Drangajökli (The Visitors Book Jökulskinna at Hrolleifsborg, Drangajökull). Jökull 219-225. Reykjavík.
  - 1969. Ísing skipa. Hafísinn 439-469. Reykjavík.
  - 1969. Icing of Ships. Jökull, 107-120. Reykjavík

Benediktsson, Jakob, 1968. Gerðir Landnámabókar. Reykjavík.

Björnsson, Axel; 1976: Jarðhræringar við Kröflu. Náttúrufræðingurinn, 4.tbl. 1976.

Björnsson, Axel; Johnsen, Gunnar; Sigurdsson, Sven; Thorbergsson, Gunnar; and Tryggvason, Eysteinn: 1979: Rifting of the Plate Boundary in North Iceland 1975-1978. Journal of Geophysical Research, June 1979.

Björnsson, A., Sæmundsson, K., Einarsson, P., Tryggvason, E., and Grönvold K. 1977: Current rifting episode in North-Iceland, Nature 266;318-323.

Björnsson, H. 1974: Explanation of jökulhlaups from Grimsvötn, Vatnajökull, Iceland. Jökull, 24: 1-26.

Björnsson, Sigurður. 1962. Undirvarp. (With English summary.) Jökull 44-45 Reykjavík..

Drift Ice and Climate. Symposium held in Reykjavik from January 27 to February 7, 1969. Dedicated to the Memory of Jón Eythorsson. Abridged versions of most of the 30 lectures presented were published in English in the 1969 issue of Jökull, Journal of the Iceland Glaciological Society, Reykjavík.
In the book Hafísinn (The Drift Ice), Reykjavík 1969, the lectures were published in Icelandic.

Dyson, James L., 1963. The World of Ice. London.

Einarsson, Trausti. 1948. Bergmyndunarsaga Vestmannaeyja. Árbók Ferðafélags Íslands: 131-157. Reykjavík..
  - 1961. Upphaf Íslands og blágrýtismyndunin. Náttúra Íslands, 11-29. Reykjavík.
  - 1961. Geysir og Geysisgos. Árbók Ferðafélags Íslands,. Reykjavík..

Einarsson, Þorleifur, 1965. Gosið í Surtsey í máli og myndum. Reykjavík.
  - 1971: Jarðfræði (Geology). Reykjavík.

Eyþórsson (Eythorsson), Jón, 1931. On the present position of the Glaciers in Iceland. Reykjavik. .
  - 1960. Vatnajökull. Reykjavík.
  - 1961. Verðurfar. Náttúra Islands, 141-154. Reykjavík.
  - 1961. Jöklar. Náttúra Íslands, 155-168. Reykjavík.
  - 1962. Norður yfir Vatnajökul 1875, W. L.Watts, Reykjavik

Friðriksson (Fridriksson), Sturla. 1967. Life and its Development on the Volcanic Island Surtsey. In: Proeeedings of the Surtsey Research Conference, Reykjavik 1967,.p. 7-19.
  - 1975: Surtsey. Evolution of life on a Volcanic Island, Butterworths, London.
  - 1987: Plant Colonization of a Volcanic Island, Surtsey, Iceland. Arctic and Alpine Research, Colorado.
  - 1989: The Volcanic Island of Surtsey, Iceland, a Quarter-century After it 'Rose from the Sea'. Environmental Conservation, Switzerland.

Groen, P., 1967. The Waters of the Sea. London.

Hafís við Ísland (collective authorship), 1968. Reykjavík.
Hafísinn (collective authorship), 1969. Reykjavík.

Jóhannsson, Guðgeir. 1919. Kötlugosið 1918. Reykjavík.

Jónsson, Jón. 1961. Jarðhiti. Náttúra Íslands. 95-119. Reykjavík.

Jónsson, Ólafur. 1945. Ódáðahraun I, II, III. - Kverkfjöll (I),
  - 1946. Frá Kröflu. Náttúrufræðingurinn, 152-157. Reykjavík.
  - 1962. Dyngjufjöll og Askja. Akureyri.

Jökull, ársrlt Jöklarannsóknafélags Íslands. 1951-1990.(Journal of Iceland Glaciological Society). Reykjavík.

Kjartansson, Guðmundur. 1943. Jarðsaga, Árnesingasaga I Reykjavík.
  - 1945. Hekla. Árbók Ferðafélags Íslands. Reykjavík. 119,
  - 1947 Þættir af Heklugosinu, Náttúrufræðingurinn. Rvk.
  - 1948. Þættir af Heklugosinu. Náttúrufræðingurinn. Reykjavík..
  - 1966. Stapakenningin og Surtsey. Náttúrufræðingurinn.
    (Summary: A Comparison of Tablemountains in Iceland and the Volcanic Island of Surtsey off the South Coast of Iceland).
Reykjavík.

Kristjánsson, Andrés. 1963. Geysir á Bárðarbungu. Reykjavík.

Kristjánsson, Leó, 1976: Marine magnetic surveys off the west coast of Iceland. Soc. Sci. Isl. Greinar V. Reykjavik.

ICELANDIC SUMMARY
ís og eldur
ÍSLENSK SAMANTEKT

land elds og ísa (bls.7).

Oft er Ísland nefnt land elds og ísa. Nafnið hlaut það af hafísnum, en hefði einnig getað dregið nafnið af jöklunum, sem þekja 11,5% af stærð þess. En í iðrum jarðar geymir það eld, jafnvel undir jökulhjúp. Þessar sérstæðu andstæður , ís og eldur eru sýndar á korti Guðbrands biskups Þorlákssonar sem gert er fyrir 1585. Saga íslensku þjóðarinnar hefur allt frá landnámstíð verið saga baráttu við náttúruöflin, ís og elda. Kunnar eru um 150 eldstöðvar, sem gosið hafa eftir ísöld. Á síðustu öldum hafa verið eldgos á Íslandi að jafnaði fimmta hvert ár. Háhitasvæði eru alls 15 á landinu, en hverir og laugar á um 700 stöðum.

hafís (bls.9).

Eiginlegur hafís myndast, þegar efsta lag sjávarins frýs.Borgarís er hinsvegar ís, sem skriðjöklar skila til sjávar. Gerð sjávaríss er breytileg eftir ytri aðstæðum, svo sem seltu, hitastigi loftsins og vindi. Í sjávarísi er mikill fjöldi af smáholum með saltlegi í.

ísrek (bls.10).

Frá Norður-Íshafinu kemur helkaldur Austur-Grænlands-straumurinn, og ber með sér mikið magn af hafís, sem stundum leggst upp að Íslandsströndum.

hafísinn og Island (bls.12).

Landnámabók segir frá því hvernig Ísland hlaut nafn sitt af hafísnum, Hafískomur eru nefndar víða í fornum annálum, en seint á nítjándu öld er farið að safna hafísfréttum án tengsla við aðra viðburði. Nú er fylgst náið með hafískomum og hafstraumum, sem stundum bera hann að ströndum landsins.

jöklar (bls.28).

Jöklar hafa frá fyrstu tíð Íslandsbyggðar þótt tignarlegir til að sjá, þar sem þá ber fannhvíta við himin úr byggð. Talið er að Íslendingar hafi raunverulega skilið myndun og eðli jökla fyrstir manna. Ef sumt af því sem ritað var um jökla á íslensku hefði verið birt á erlendu heimsmáli hefði það þótt athyglisverður skerfur til jöklafræði þeirra tíma. Jöklar hylja um 11800 km², eða um 11,5% af öllu landinu.

skriðjöklar (bls.33).

Skriðjöklar eru afrennsli hájöklanna.Undan fargi sígur ísinn af fjalllendi niður í dali og láglendi, þar til hitinn bræðir hann og jafnvægi næst við jökulsporðinn milli skriðs og leysingar. Sprungusvæði myndast þar sem skriðjökull fer yfir klettabelti.Stundum skríður skriðjökul-sporður niður í vötn eða lón. Ísjakar brotna þar oft af sporðinum, fljóta um vatnið og bráðna, eða halda áleiðis til sjávar með jökulánum.

Snæfellsjökull (bls.43).

Yst á Snæfellsnesi gnæfir hann 1446 m yfir sjó, snækrýnd eldkeila, en hefur ekki gosið síðan land byggðist. Fræg skáldsaga franska skáldsins Jules Verne um leyndardóma Snæfellsjökuls, segir þar vera opna leið í iður jarðar.

Vatnajökull (bls.51).

Langstærsti jökull á Íslandi, um 8400 km². Meginhluti Vatnajökuls er nokkuð jöfn hjarnjökulbunga. Hæsta jökulbungan er Bárðarbunga um 2000 m há. Upp úr megin jöklinum rísa einstök jökulsker og fjallgarðar. Jökultungur skriðjöklanna teygja sig út úr hjarnbreiðunni allsstaðar þar sem randfjöllin halda ekki á móti.

veðrið á jökli (bls.57).

Á jökli getur verið hörkufrost og blindhríð á hvaða tíma árs sem er, en þar getur allt eins verið slydda og rigning. En svo koma þar dagar, þegar sólin brennhitar svo allt og alla, að menn fækka klæðum þótt hættan á sólbruna sé mikil. En svo er þessi einkennilega skuggalausa birta, þegar þoka leggst yfir jökulinn.Engir skuggar sjást. Þetta fyrirbæri er nefnt hvítblinda.

Grímsvötn (bls.58).

Undir jökulhjúpi Vatnajökuls eru virk eldgosasvæði. Þar er eldur undir ísi. Þekktast þeirra eru Grímsvötn, sem eru sig-dæld vestantil við miðbik jökulsins. Í þessa kvos safnast mikið vatnsmagn milli eldgosa, að mestu frá bráðnun jökulsins vegna hita frá hverasvæði. Mikil jökulhlaup verða frá Grímsvötnum og flæðir vatnið þá undir jökul og kemur fram undan Skeiðarárjökli.

rannsóknir (bls.62).

Jöklarannsóknir eru margþættar. Fylgst er með vexti og rýrnun jöklanna og hreyfingum skriðjöklanna.Borkjarnar eru rannsakaðir. Árlög jöklanna veita heimildir um veðurfar langt aftur í tímann. Með öskulögum í jökulísi má tímasetja eldgos.

jökulslóðir (bls.64).

Forðum daga fóru menn gangandi eða á skíðum og á hestbaki yfir jökla. Nú eru mest notaðir snjóbílar, vélsleðar og sérlega útbúnir fjórhjóladrifnir bílar til jöklaferða, bæði til rannsókna-ferða og skemmtiferða.

snjór verður ís (bls.66).

Snjór sem fellur á jökul breytist smátt og smátt í hjarn og síðan ís undir fargi. Djúpt í jökli er harður ís með mikið af loftbólum.

ísfletir (bls.70).

Frost,sólbráð og vindar umskapa yfirborð jökla á ýmsan hátt.

Öræfajökull   (bls,74).

Öræfajökull er eldjall, sem gosið hefur tvisvar síðan land byggðist. Þar er Hvannadalshnjúkur, 2110 m, hæsti tindur Íslands. Þaðan er að sjálfsögðu frábært útsýni.

jökullón   (bls.84).

Jökullón myndast oft við rætur skriðjökla, þegar þeir hopa vegna hlýnandi veðurfars. Þá myndast einnig jökullón þegar skriðjökull stíflar hliðardal, sem síðan safnar í sig vatni.

vetrarsnjór   (bls.88).

Vetrarsnjórinn er árviss í borg og sveit á norðlægum slóðum.Skíðamenn fagna honum og í fjalllendi dregur hann fram heildarlínur í landslaginu. Vetrarsnjórinn getur því verið heillandi og til fegurðarauka, þótt oft sé hann til óþurftar og kostnaðarauka fyrir einstaklinga og þjóðfélagsheildina.

ísing   (bls.96).

Ísing getur verið margbreytileg. Alkunn gerð ísingar eru grýlukerti, sem verða til þar sem vatn drýpur í frosti. Í hraunhellum eru slíkar ísmyndanir oft stórkostlegar. Þá er hrím á trjágróðri orðlagt fyrir fegurð í skini morgunsólar.

klakabönd   (bls.99).

Veturinn færir fossana í nýjan búning. Í langvarandi frostum skreytir fossúðinn umhverfið með fjölbreytilegri klakabrynju.

hverir undir ís   (bls.100).

Víða eru hverir undir ís, sem þeir bræða frá sér og mynda íshella. Kunnir staðir af þessu tagi eru Kverkfjöll og Hrafntinnusker nálægt Landmannalaugum.

vatnið   (bls.102).

vatnið kemur fyrir í náttúru Íslands í öllum þess myndum, sem frosið í hafís og jöklum, vökvi í ám og vötnum og sem gufa í hverum. Vatnið er lífgjafi gróðurs og dýra. Stórfossar landsins er hrífandi sjón, en fegurðar má líka njóta við tæran fjallalæk.

Kverkfjöll   (bls.105).

Þetta fjalllendi er gömul eldstöð, efalítið ennþá virk. Þar eru einhver mestu háhitasvæði landsins, með miklum gufu- og leirhverum.Þar eru víða hverir undir ís í jaðri Vatnajökuls.

líparít   (bls.111).

Líparít er litskrúðugt storkuberg. Það getur verið sterkgult, bleikt, rauðleitt, gráblátt eða grænt.

leirhverir   (bls.112).

Háhitasvæði landsins eru oft nefnd gufuhverasvæði. Þau einkennast af brennisteinshverum, gufuhverum og leirhverum, og háhitasvæði virðast öll vera nátengd nýlegum eldsumbrotum.

goshverir   (bls.117).

Frægastur goshver er Geysir í Haukadal, og þar er líka Strokkur og fleiri goshverir, en þeir eru líka víðar á háhitasvæðum.

244

eldstöðvar   (bls.121).

Undir öllum eldstövum er bergkvika (magma), sem talin er vera þar í fljótandi formi. Í eldgosum brýst bergkvikan upp í gegn um efri berglög og upp á yfirborð jarðar. Getur úr sömu bergkviku bæði komið hraunrennsli og mismunandi gjóska (laus gosefni).Fjöldi íslenskra eldstöðva hefur verið áætlaður örugglega yfir 150, en sennilega eru þær fleiri en 200. Frægasta eldstöð landsins er Hekla, sem gosið hefur margoft á sögulegum tíma. Mikið gos var í Heklu 1947, en minni gos í og við Heklu 1970, 1980-81 og 1991. - Lakagígar mynduðust í Skaftáreldum 1783. Það er langstærsta hraungos, sem menn hafa augum litið. Hraunið þekur 565 km² landssvæði og rúmmál þess er áætlað 12,3 km³. - Oft er getið jarðelda í Dyngjufjöllum og í Öskju, en þar gaus við Öskjuop 1961.

Surtsey,eldgos í hafi 1963   (bls.134).

Eldgos hófst á hafsbotni 14.nóvember 1963 um 33 km undan Landeyjarsandi og 23 km frá Heimaey. Þar varð til ný eyja, þar sem áður var 130 m dýpi. Surtseyjargosi lauk 5.júní 1967, og hafði þá staðið svo til samfleitt í 3 ár og nærri 7 mánuði. Þá var flatarmál Surtseyjar 2,8 km². Síðan hefur hafaldan og vindur mótað eyna, aska breyst í móberg og gróður fest rætur.

eldur í Heklu 1970   (bls.174).

Stutt eldgos varð í Heklu 1970.

Hekla gýs 1980-81   (bls.180).

Aftur stutt eldgos í Heklu 1980 og 1981. Talið vera sama eldgosið, þótt nokkurt hlé væri á milli.

Grímsvötn, eldgos 1983   (bls.188).

Stutt eldgos undir Vatnajökli, í Grímsvötnum 1983.

Heimaey, eldgos 1973   (bls.191).

Eldsprunga opnaðist að morgni 23.janúar 1973, aðeins um 200 m frá Kirkjubæjunum, austustu byggð Vestmannaeyjakapstaðar. Aldrei hefur eldgos hafist svo nærri þéttbýli á Íslandi og í þessu gosi. Mikil gjóska féll yfir bæinn. Eldfjallið Eldfell hlóðst upp og hraun rann yfir austasta hluta bæjarins.-Strax að gosi loknu var hafist handa við að hreinsa bæinn og síðar sama ár var atvinnulífið í Verstmannaeyjum svipað og fyrir gos.

Krafla, eldgos 1975-84   (bls.215).

Kröflugos hófust að morgni 20.desember 1975, þegar sprunga opnaðist norðan Leirhnjúks. Til ársloka 1981 urðu 8 eldgos í Kröfluöskjunni með hléum á milli. Síðan varð 9. eldgosið 4. september 1984, og því lauk 18.september. Þá hafði hraun frá þessum eldgosum runnið yfir 36 km² svæði og heildar rúmmál var áætlað um 0,25 km³. Gliðnun lands var um 4-5 m.

Hekla, eldgos 1991   (bls.229).

Enn hófst eldgos í Heklu 17.janúar 1991.Í upphafi var töluvert hraungos, en strax á öðrum degi hafði dregið verulega úr því, og eftir það gaus aðeins á einum stað.Hraunflóð alls 23 km².

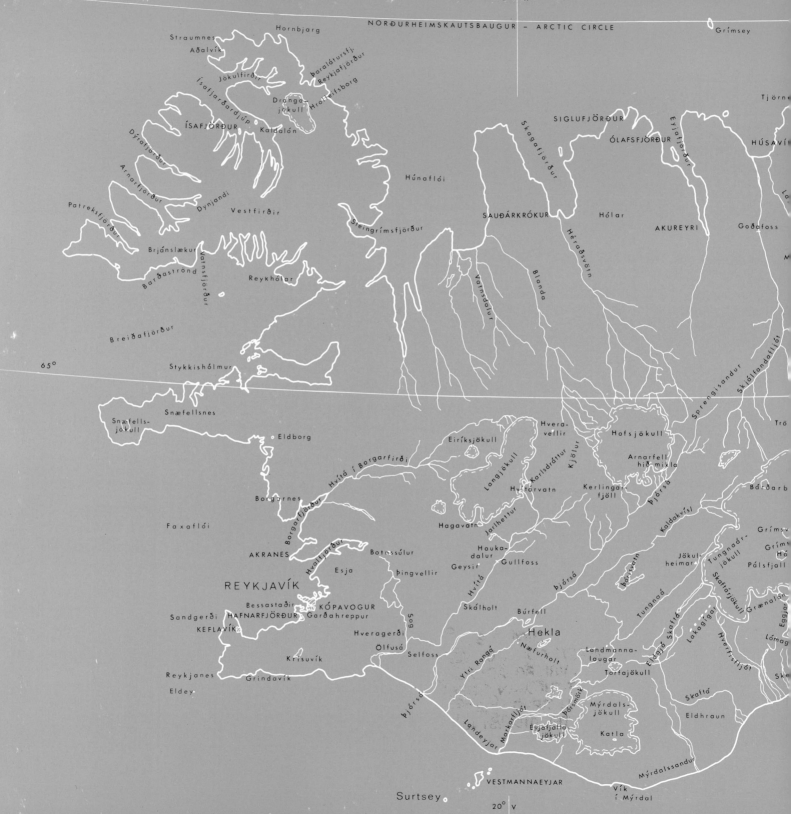

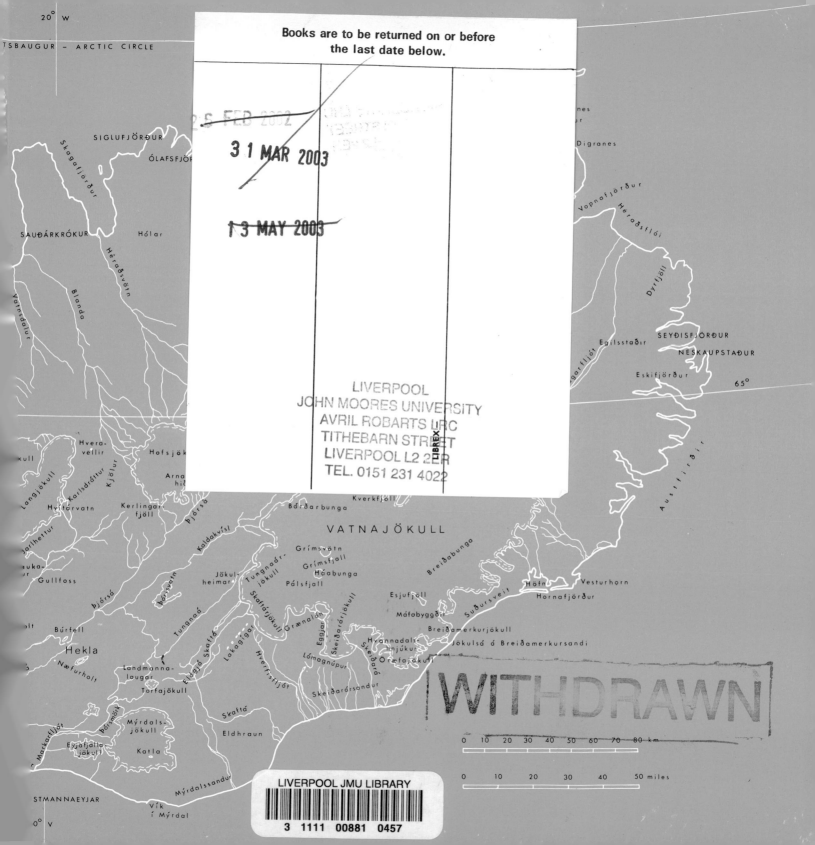